MEN WHO PIONEERED INVENTIONS

"Makers of Our Modern World" Books

By Lynn and Gray Poole

SCIENTISTS WHO CHANGED THE WORLD

SCIENTISTS WHO WORK OUTDOORS

SCIENTISTS WHO WORK WITH ASTRONAUTS

SCIENTISTS WHO WORK WITH CAMERAS

DOCTORS WHO SAVED LIVES

MEN WHO DIG UP HISTORY

MEN WHO PIONEERED INVENTIONS

By Edna Yost

WOMEN OF MODERN SCIENCE

MODERN AMERICANS IN SCIENCE AND TECHNOLOGY

By Eleanor Clymer and Lillian Erlich

MODERN AMERICAN CAREER WOMEN

MEN WHO
PIONEERED INVENTIONS

By *LYNN* and *GRAY POOLE*

Illustrated

DODD, MEAD & COMPANY · *NEW YORK*

Library of Congress Catalog Card: 69-17604

Printed in the United States of America
by The Haddon Craftsmen, Inc., Scranton, Penna.

This book is for
BEN COHEN
and
HERMAN COHEN

CONTENTS

ILLUSTRATIONS

Galileo Galilei,
1564-1642

Right: Telescope designed
by Galileo who built hun-
dreds of the instruments

Far Right: Thermometer invented by Santorio Santorre,
1561-1636

Anton van Leeuwenhoek, 1632-1723

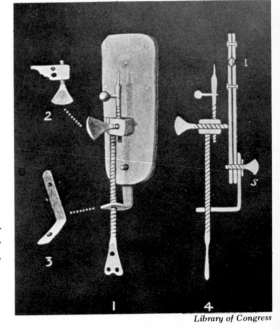

Leeuwenhoek's invention that opened the way for scientific study by microscope

James Watt,
1736-1819

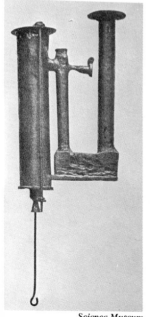

The original model of Watt's surface condenser
engine

Camera invented by
Niepce

Joseph Nicéphore Niepce, 1765-1833 (Portrait by C.
Laguiche)

The calculating machine of Charles Babbage was a forerunner of today's computer

Library of Congress

Charles Babbage, 1792-1871

Library of Congress

Christopher Latham Sholes,
1819-1890

Sholes sold his rights to his typewriter invention to E. Remington
and Sons, makers of the first commercial machine

Howe's sewing machine incorporated basic principles still in use

Elias Howe, 1819-1867

Samuel Pierpont Langley, 1834-1906

Langley's Aerodrome #5 before launch (1896)

Langley's manned aerodrome crashes with pilot Charles M. Manley in 1903

Ottmar Mergenthaler, 1854-1899

Mergenthaler Blower
Linotype (1886)

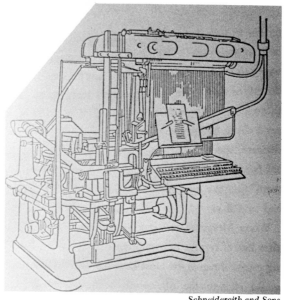

Schneidereith and Sons

Johns Hopkins University

Mergenthaler Lino-
type

Gottlieb Daimler,
1834-1900

Daimler-Benz, A. G. Archives

Karl Benz, 1844-1929

Daimler-Benz, A. G. Archives

Benz's motor vehicle of 1893 with the inventor's daughter, Clara, at the controls

Daimler's motor vehicle with four wheels, 1886

John Logie Baird, 1888-1946

Baird's original television transmitter given by the inventor to the Science Museum in South Kensington

Vladimir Kosma Zworykin (1889-   ) and his television tube

Thomas Alva Edison (1847-1931) examining film strip of his motion picture machine

MEN WHO PIONEERED INVENTIONS

Inventions kindle controversy. The pages of their history abound with contradictions, inevitable and understandable. Very few inventions can be given clear-cut attribution to one man or can be precisely pinpointed by a single date. Most major inventions incorporate concepts or components conceived by men other than the credited inventor, so dating demarcations vary. But the challengeable credit and the debatable date are inconsequential in the light of an actual invention that effects major changes in man's way of life. The preliminary to invention is often dramatic, and the climax of individual success, ever exciting.

In-depth study of inventions reveals justification for the contradictions that confuse people who casually look up, in more than one source book, the date and the name of the originator of this or that invention. Those who write about inventors have no choice but to single out, according to their own judgment, the outstanding creative and imaginative men who significantly contributed to specific inventions. Although the decisions are sometimes arbitrary, the men chosen deserve recognition for their ingenuity and dedication.

For this book we selected popularly known inventors like

Galileo and Edison, and inventors of restricted reputation like Niepce and Babbage. All merit the respect with which they are today regarded in those disciplines of science or branches of technology benefiting from their contributions. Unique for respective reasons, they have in common the distinction of recognized achievement. Rich men or poor, scholars or school dropouts, good fellows or crusty recluses, they pioneered progress.

Relative importance is another matter of dissension about inventions, and once more decisions have to be discretionary. Man's present way of life could not have been established without the thirteen inventions discussed in this book. They are variously fundamental to communications media, transportation, space exploration, mass manufacture and to research, in the laboratory and in the field. Fervid proponents, challenging our selections, will make valid claims for other inventions: the telegraph and the telephone, the printing press and the steamboat, the rocket and the loom. Those and many other inventions are of undeniable merit, but so too are those presented here.

Although inventions and scientific discovery differ, some few inventors have also been discoverers. Discovery is the revelation of a phenomenon previously unknown, or the first recognition and utilization of an existent property. An invention is the creation of a thing; it is a device conceived by man and made practical by his methods.

The inventor may be a master of the imaginative concept, depending on technicians to carry forward the execution of his brilliant design. More often he is dexterous and mechanically skilled, evidencing his facility at a very young age.

Precocious tinkerers are predominant in this book, and their early experimentations were carried out in home workshops and makeshift laboratories, often with the encouragement of understanding parents.

Certain similarities in the circumstances of the inventors included here serve to point up the exceptions. Few had formal advanced education and an intellectual heritage. Poor health and family poverty caused several to leave school when children; some were apprenticed at trades that proved to be of later value even if not directly related to the subsequent invention. Most were expert with their hands and experimented during their lives with more than one invention. A number had brothers who shared their interests, if not always contributing to the invention; the cooperating brother, providing an extra pair of hands for mechanical tasks, was the sounding board for theories and the catalyst for ideas.

Frustration, disappointment and dejection were common to those who experienced trial-and-error failures, mechanical breakdowns, scornful criticism and lack of understanding. Persistence was the prevailing characteristic. Against long odds and in the face of derision, these men sustained to practical conclusion the inventions which, in several instances, others had thought of or even patented, and then abandoned, lacking either courage or foresight to continue.

As a skein of comparison links the inventors, so a pattern outlines the progression of the inventions. From the early sixteenth century until well into the eighteenth, there was an overlapping of techniques and methods, of devices and mechanisms. Scholarly communities kept abreast of research and experimentation within their own confines and abroad. A professor leaving one university post for another in his own country spread the news of contemporary research. Intellectuals traveling throughout Europe gathered facts from learned societies and made lengthy observations at laboratories, reporting by correspondence and in later conference on the up-to-date scientific discoveries and mechanical inventions of foreign scholars. The propensity for sharing information was aptly expressed by Anton Van Leeuwenhoek in the seventeenth century: ". . . wherever I found out anything remarkable, I have thought it my duty to put down my discovery on paper so that all ingenious people might be informed thereof."

Colonization around the world and settlement in the Americas, particularly in the United States, expanded the range of scholars in one sense, but lessened their interchange of ideas and philosophies. Theories and inventions independently emerged at widespread geographical locations without those involved being aware of the existence of a similar study or experimental project elsewhere.

In the nineteenth century, an increase in the number of scholarly journals published and the improvement of transportation facilities, on land and sea, made it possible again for scholars to be informed about the research of their foreign peers. There was at the same time an incredible lack of communication among inventors. Elias Howe experimenting with his sewing machine in Massachusetts apparently did not know about the invention of Walter Hunt who lived in nearby New York State. Later in the century, Karl Benz and Gottfried Daimler made no effort to meet for the exchange of views on automobile design, production and manufacture;

both were well known in their native Germany, and each must have been aware of the other's work.

Samuel Langley, an American contemporary of Benz and Daimler, held the earlier view of spreading knowledge, even to informing the general public. He wrote, in 1877: "Science is not just for the professional student alone. Everyone will take an interest in its results if they are only put before the world in the right way."

Inventions are now "put before the world" in every way. In this twentieth century, air travel, television transmitted by satellite and the transoceanic telephone can make available to scholars and inventors, almost simultaneously with the fact, information about like research and experimentation going on in distant countries on other continents.

An invention of far-reaching importance may issue today from a dingy loft workroom or from a laboratory sparsely equipped, but announcement of its existence will be immediate. There is one other certainty about any invention of today or tomorrow: It will be controversial, stirring up arguments about attribution, prior claim, patent infringement, originality, practicability. That is the history of invention.

Thermometric study is essential to human welfare because all people on earth are affected by temperature, natural or man-made.

SANTORIO SANTORRE
1561–1636, Italian

CORNELIUS DREBBEL
1572–1634, Dutch

Through the ages, thousands of pounds of paper have been filled with words attempting to pinpoint the invention of the thermometer. The claims of proponents of one or another scientist as the thermometer's inventor clearly illustrate how difficult it is to assign the origin of a basic instrument to a specific person.

Search for the thermometer's inventor reverts to ancient Greece: to Aristotle, the philosopher-scientist, pupil of Plato and tutor of Alexander the Great. In the fourth century B.C., Aristotle puzzled about temperature; questioned why there were two extremes, hot and cold; and tried to develop a method for recording degrees of difference between the two.

In the second century B.C., both Philo of Byzantium and Hero of Alexandria attempted to measure varying degrees of temperature through application of theories of pneumatics, the study of air, its temperatures and pressures. The written records of the pneumatics research of Philo and Hero were long lost, then retrieved, and eventually translated for scientific scholars to read and study.

The Hellenic scientist Galen left another permanent record of temperature investigation, done in the second century A.D. Galen tried to establish fixed temperature points between the extremes of hot and cold, setting a neutral point by an experiment of beautiful simplicity: the addition of ice to boiling water. Lacking sophisticated instrumentation, he assigned various numbers of intermediary degrees of temperature. "Assigned" is the exact word because Galen's *logical points* between the extremes of temperature were arrived at by reasoning and guesswork.

With every passing century men of science were curious about temperatures of the human body, of weather, and of natural and man-made objects. How many men, by the hundreds, tried to devise a means for actual measurement of *fixed points* between hot and cold can never be known. Many worked with variations of the *thermoscope,* forerunner of the thermometer.

The thermoscope showed that liquid, when heated in a container, expands and rises; when heat is withdrawn, the liquid contracts and lowers. The instruments, generally made of glass, consisted of a bulb and an open-end perpendicular tube. When the bulb was heated, water rose in the tube; the water level was lowered by the removal of the heat source, sometimes only body temperature of the human hand.

Boring repetition of the elementary experiment with

water in a thermoscope must have vexed those who heated the water by one means or another, and then let the water cool. Frustration was the lot of men unable to establish a consistent specific point of water level. In vain, generation after generation of experimenters tried to design an instrument in which a liquid would rise to a fixed point by the application of a specific amount of controlled heat. Arbitrarily assigned fixed points were etched on the perpendicular tubes of hundreds of thermoscopes to no avail. There was not to be a breakthrough until the seventeenth century when scientific investigation bloomed.

Scientists, interested in temperature research, avidly studied Hero's *Pneumatics* immediately after its publication in Latin, in 1575. It was translated into Italian in 1589, and a second Italian translation appeared in 1592. The work was a handbook for scientists seeking answers to questions about relative degrees, the range of the extremes of hot and cold.

One fact about the invention of the thermometer is certain: In spite of conflicting claims, Galileo Galilei did not invent the instrument. The famed astronomer, physicist and mathematician (1564–1642) had a personality and nature that so endeared him to his students that they were prone to attribute to him all firsts of ideas and inventions.

Galileo's boundless curiosity led him to limitless inquiry into natural phenomena, including temperature. He did, in fact, study *Pneumatics* in 1592, the year he became a professor at the University of Padua, where he gave a lecture-demonstration on liquids and their reactions to temperature and pressure. Along with numerous other experiments he demonstrated the principle of the thermoscope, using a hand-held instrument, crude in design. The water in the bulb, heated by the temperature of Galileo's palm, expanded and rose in the tube; the professor set down the thermoscope, the liquid cooled, and the water level fell.

By correspondence, many former pupils of Galileo's kept him informed about scientific experimentations going on in many parts of Europe. Two interested in temperature studies were Giovanfrancesco Sagredo and Daniello Antonini.

In 1612, Sagredo saw an instrument for measuring the temperature of liquids in the University of Venice laboratory of Professor Santorio Santorre, more familiarly known as Santorius. In a letter to Galileo, Sagredo described "an instrument of Santorius' with which cold and heat are measured by means of a compass [i.e., measuring device] . . . a large bulb with a long neck." The device of Santorius' had fixed points "to which water always rises and remains under specific application of heat."

That same year Santorre moved his laboratory to Padua, but Galileo was gone, having taken a professorship at the University of Florence. Corresponding with Galileo about improvements of the thermoscope, Sagredo tried unsuccessfully for five years to duplicate the device of Santorre. Meanwhile, Galileo infrequently demonstrated his own simple thermoscope for the benefit of his students at Florence.

Santorre made a thermometer, its date given as 1611. But historians of science have to question whether it was the first. Among a stack of musty papers found in a library at Rome, there was an unpublished and unsigned manuscript which not only described but illustrated a true thermometer. The document was dated 1611. The device, sealed at both ends, fulfilled the basic requirements of a thermometer; the liquid-filled glass tube was etched with numbers on an ascending scale from hot to cold.

The European community of scholars of the seventeenth century was in constant communication by letter and by word of mouth from scientist travelers. Especially in Italy, the shifting of professors from one university to another simplified the exchange of information about research in numerous places. That being so, the 1611 thermometer presents a mystery. Why was it never mentioned by scholars studying temperatures? The most educated guess is that the Roman investigator was either an amateur or a solitary. He could hardly have been an established scholar whose reputation and accomplishments made him eligible for a university post.

Santorre probably was the inventor of the first known thermometer. A nameless Roman may have been. The search of historians for other claimants leads far to the north, to England and to Holland. A strong contender is Robert Fludd (sometimes Flud), born in Wales.

After study at Oxford University in England and on the Continent, Fludd (1574–1637) settled in London and practiced as a physician. He was much influenced by Paracelsus, the sixteenth-century Swiss physician, theologist, alchemist, chemist and metallurgist. The arrogant and heretical Paracelsus, although contemptuous of established theories of medicine, made significant medical contributions with his treatment of goiter, of syphilis and of paralysis resulting from head injuries. Fludd was more fascinated by the mystical theories of Paracelsus than by his scientific accomplishments, and ironically some writers, scholarly and popular, emphasize Fludd's own mysticism rather than his indefatigable investigation of scientific subjects.

Paracelsus stated unequivocally that spiritual and physical truths were identical, and to that thesis Fludd subscribed, holding that there was a center of one God. The manifestations of the one God were man and the world, a world created by lesser deities in the hierarchy. Through evangelism, Fludd converted thousands to his Rosicrucian beliefs; by promotion, he popularized his chemical prescriptions for cure-all medicines.

Objective historians of science credit Fludd with experimentation in temperature measurement. He read the translations of Philo's writings on pneumatics now in Oxford's Bodleian Library, and wrote commentaries about temperature gauges he had heard about or seen. Papers written by Fludd were illustrated with drawings of his inventions, purported to be thermometers. The instruments, although crude and undependable for consistent recording of temperatures ranging from hot to cold, were nonetheless thermometers.

Cornelius Drebbel, of Holland, working contemporaneously with Fludd, was a highly skilled, intuitive and creative inventor. His popular recognition came with the creation of a perpetual timepiece, famed throughout Europe when it was built. King James I of England, having heard about the ingenuity of Drebbel, invited the Dutch inventor to the royal court at Eltham. There Drebbel constructed an intricate, beautiful and, in every way, astounding astronomical clock. Its action depended on a sealed glass tube in which liquid contracted and expanded to power the mechanism. Many men mistakenly thought the tube's functioning was regulated by the rising and falling of tides.

Daniello Antonini, onetime student of Galileo's, traveling from Brussels to England to examine the astronomical clock, reported on it to his former professor. In a letter dated February 1, 1612, he wrote about the perpetual motion device "in which a liquid moves inside a glass tube . . . after the manner of the tides, it is said." Subsequently, having given serious thought to the fluctuating liquid in Drebbel's power tube, Antonini expressed to Galileo his doubt of the tide theory. "I thought that the truth might be that this motion comes from a change in the air, namely that which is caused by the fluctuation of heat and cold." In yet a later letter, Antonini included a sketch of the tube which powered Drebbel's self-winding astronomical clock. That sketch prompted Galileo to demonstrate once again the principle of the thermoscope for his students.

Drebbel, meanwhile, shuttled often between the British Isles and the Low Countries, where an instrument for measuring temperatures was widely known and generally used in the second decade of the seventeenth century. The instrument, common in Belgium and Holland, was similar to that used by Drebbel in the clock of King James I. Available records offer no proof that Drebbel actually created the temperature-measuring instrument, but respected historians think that it was, at least, based on Drebbel's original design.

The instrument for measuring temperature was called a *thermometer*, the word being first used by Jean Leurcheron, a Jesuit priest who published scientific papers under the pseudonym H. Van Etten. A 1625 treatise by Van Etten contained an illustration of an Italian unscaled thermoscope beside the Dutch scaled thermometer.

Historical evidence indicates that Santorio Santorre, Cornelius Drebbel, and an unknown Roman share the honor of being the inventor of a thermometer with a fixed scale, a scale practical for measuring the intermediate degrees between extremes of hot and cold. An inability to pinpoint one man as the original inventor of the thermometer bears out the sage, if vernacular, observation of an uneducated man who, after watching a 1954 television program on basic research, said, "I never thought of it before, but it takes a heck of a lotta guys, workin' in a lotta places, to find hundreds a facts before one guy can announce sumpin amazin'."

The invention of a calibrated thermometer, an instrument marked with degrees from hot to cold, challenged scientists. They were aware of the need for development of a sealed thermometer where air from outside did not directly act on the liquid in the perpendicular glass column, and for a thermometer that would function everywhere: at all latitudes, longitudes and altitudes. Scientists wanted an instrument for countless temperature experiments around the world in which the results could be understood and applied by scientists everywhere. Those men who experimented with temperature measurements in an outstanding scientific age include Robert Hooke, Edmund Halley, Christiaan Huygens, Isaac Newton and Ferdinand II, Duke of Tuscany.

Ferdinand II and his brother Leopold, members of the famous Medici family, belonged to the Florence Academy of Science, and both were greatly respected by scientists of their day. The reputation of the brothers as sincere, dedicated and painstaking scientific investigators endures to the present.

It was Ferdinand II who invented a sealed thermometer in 1654, producing the first practical instrument of its kind. In the late seventeenth century, the Florentine's thermometer was studied in detail by Sir Robert Boyle, President of the Royal Society, London. After a thorough examination of the instrument's design, and following repeated tests of its capabilities, Sir Robert pronounced it an "original work of immeasurable significance."

In the development of the discipline of thermometry, three men stand out as titans: René-Antoine Ferchault de Réaumur (1683–1757), Gabriel Daniel Fahrenheit (1686–1736), and Anders Celsius (1701–1744). Each made a lasting scientific contribution: a thermometer still in use.

Réaumur, born in France, spent his professional life investigating a multiplicity of scientific phenomena. An early contribution was proof that a thermometer registers degrees of hotness and coldness in direct proportion to its size. Réaumur constructed his thermometer in various sizes, each registering specific degrees by established difference in spaces between its fixed degree points. The instrument was used by him in distillation of French wines and for testing the temperatures of numerous other liquids. The sealed tube of Réaumur's thermometer contained alcohol, its rising and falling dependent on the range of temperature.

After years of experimentation, Réaumur settled on two fixed points with eighty median points between the extremes: On the Réaumur scale 0° R. is the freezing point and 80° R., the boiling point. Opposing the fixed points set by other experimenters, Réaumur proved the validity and workability of his own thermometer with its eighty points between boiling and freezing.

Fahrenheit, a native of Danzig, Germany, was first renowned throughout Europe as a skilled maker of precision instruments; later, he became a physician of great achievements. Like many others, Fahrenheit was eager to produce an instrument ideal for registering change on the temperature scale. While on a lecture tour of Denmark, Fahrenheit visited the laboratory of the distinguished Danish astronomer Ole Roemer, who demonstrated his own thermometer, an instrument with which he was trying to set a degree-range that would be universally acceptable. Fahrenheit recognized both the flaws in Roemer's design and the potential merit of certain of the Dane's theories.

Applying what he learned from Roemer's instrument, Fahrenheit developed a temperature scale that could be applied to scientific investigation of the most delicate and precise order. His thermometer of 1714 had a scale of degrees ranging from 32° F., the freezing point of water, to 212° F., the boiling point of water. That thermometer is well established as the calibrated measurement for most general use in the United States.

Not long after, another thermometer was produced by the great Swedish astronomer Anders Celsius, who traveled widely to remote places, including Lapland, to make astronomical observations. He devised, primarily for his own studies, a thermometer that almost at once was accepted as an instrument invaluable to scientific researchers.

The thermometer of Celsius had a calibrated series of fixed degree points ranging from 0° C., the freezing point of water, to 100° C., the boiling point of water. The *C.,* which originally stood for Celsius, came to be known as centigrade, or the 100 points between boiling and freezing. The centigrade scale is commonly used today in Europe.

Other investigators devised thermometers with differently calculated fixed points of temperature. But, as the researchers delved into many scientific disciplines, they found the Réaumur, Fahrenheit and centigrade (Celsius) thermometers to be the most advantageous to an international scientific community. Whatever the calibration, it could easily be understood by calculating the change from one scale to another.

A nineteenth-century thermometer that attracted scientists was one introduced by William Thomson Kelvin (1824–1907), professor of natural philosophy at the University of Glasgow. His thermometer had a newly calculated fixed scale for what is known as "absolute degree temperature." Kelvin fixed his freezing point at 273° K. and his boiling point at 373° K. The range of fixed points is 100, the same spread as that of the centigrade system of Celsius, but research scientists find the Kelvin thermometer to be more precise for laboratory research; his scale of absolute degree temperature is widely used by today's scientists throughout the world.

AND AFTER

Never satisfied by a goal achieved, scientists look forward, seeking the new, the improved, the ultimate in technique and instrumentation. No sooner were thermometers standardized than scientists concentrated on experiments with other means for measuring temperature.

In this century, the need for sophisticated instruments for

measuring temperatures accelerated with the expansion of commerce, industry and travel, and with proliferating disciplines of science. For certain practical purposes, the conventional thermometer is supplanted by numerous modern devices, including the thermocouple.

Itself dependent on temperature, the thermocouple measures temperature. The thermocouple, or thermoelectric thermometer, basically consists of wires or bars of different metals, like iron and copper, or platinum and iridium, joined at their terminal points. Electromotive force is produced by keeping the conductors at different temperatures; the degree of the flow through the thermocouple is measured by a galvanometer or a potentiometer. The temperature of a third substance can be measured when it is connected to the coupling of the dissimilar metals of the thermoelectric thermometer.

Thermopile is the name for several thermocouples joined for service on large projects. The thermocouple, in all its variations, is invaluable for highly sensitive scientific investigations and for gross actions, large-scale operations, in which many temperatures of varying degrees must be simultaneously recorded at a precise time.

Thermometric study continues unceasingly because all people everywhere on earth are affected by temperature, natural and man-made. In civilized societies, every facet of daily living is dependent on temperature, its measurement and control. Devices for measuring temperature are essential to meteorology, manufacturing, scientific research, transportation, food processing, medical diagnostics and therapy, with millions of variations in those and other categories.

Galileo was a pioneer of space exploration carried out by telescopes he built for observing phenomena of the heavens.

GALILEO GALILEI
1564–1642, Italian

During a trip from Padua to Florence, a casual companion asked Galileo Galilei if he were the seventh son of a seventh son. Aware of the popular superstition attributing good fortune and great talent to such a child, Galileo answered the complimentary question with, "No, I am more fortunate. I was the first of seven born to Vincenzo of the family Bonajurti, more recently known as Galilei."

To any informed Italian, that revealing statement showed Galileo to be descended from leaders of the region around Florence. His forebears were Florentine noblemen, nineteen of whom served in high offices between 1343 and 1528. The surname was changed to Galilei after the 1343 election of Tomasso Bonajurti to the College of the Twelve Buonomini, the dozen rulers of the republic.

Nearly two centuries later, when Vincenzo Galilei was born in 1520, the honored family's financial condition was at its nadir. While impecunious, Vincenzo was proud of his heritage of scholarship and studied languages, literature, mathematics and music. He was a lute player of distinction, a composer, singer and author. One of the first to write recitatives, Vincenzo heard his own performed by the Florentine *camerata*, of which he was a member. He published critiques of the compositions of his music master, Zarlino of Chiogga, and in 1581 wrote an attack against musical counterpoint reputed to be the first ever published. None of Vincenzo's musical or literary efforts were remunerative, and it was as a cloth merchant that he supported his wife and children.

Ambitious for his firstborn son, Vincenzo undertook the early education of the child to assure for him acceptance in literary circles and attainment in scholarly pursuits. Galileo, born on February 15, 1564, in Pisa, was tutored at home almost from infancy; at his father's knee he received instructions in Greek, Latin, the arts and the sciences. Before the youngster was ten years old, he was placed under the tutelage of Jacopo Borghini, an eminent scientific scholar.

At twelve, Galileo was sent to a monastery school in Vallombrosa where, an outstanding student, he was much attracted by the monastic life. Learning of his son's religious inclination, Vincenzo summarily removed Galileo from the monastery. Continuing his studies at home, the youth spent his leisure hours designing toys, tinkering with mechanical objects, and devising mathematical games.

Under pressure from his father, Galileo entered the University of Pisa as a medical student. He was from the first at odds with those who taught the principles of Galen by rote. Frustrated by the dull method of instruction and by the passive adherence to ancient theories, Galileo, thinking for himself, arrived at conclusions often quite opposite to those of his professors. An exception was a young teacher of Euclidean mathematics who transferred to his students his own "wonder at the science of mathematics." Through increased enthusiasm for that science, Galileo was led to a deep interest in astronomy, and away from medicine.

When only in his early twenties, Galileo was already known everywhere in Italy for his ability in probing investigation, his creative approach to any scholarly problem, and for his originality in scientific inquiry. One of his intimate friends was Ostilio Ricci, a well-known tutor of noblemen; they, like Ricci and Galileo, questioned facts and theories, long unchallenged. This coterie of intellectuals and scholars was ambitious for Italians to be in the vanguard of progress in science and the humanities.

In part because of his association with progressives and in part by reason of his own rebellious attitude, Galileo failed to win an appointment as professor at the University of Bologna, a post he sought. But his undeniable ability and personal charm won him, in July, 1589, the chair of mathematics at the University of Padua. The twenty-four-year-old professor quickly made devoted and faithful disciples of students at Padua attracted by his ebullience and charisma, and impressed by his scientific perception. Outside the classroom, Galileo probed every scientific area from which he thought new knowledge might be mined, unearthing discoveries in rapid sequence. He studied the research findings and instruments of other science scholars, using the facts and devices as springboards for practical applications of his own.

Galileo's invention of the telescope originated from his examination of optical lenses arranged in a Dutch device that was little more than a plaything for adults. The instrument resulted from an accidental occurrence in the workshop of Hans Lippershey (or Lipperhey), a skillful maker of eyeglasses, at Middleburg, Holland.

Lippershey employed about one hundred artisans at his profitable establishment where, one day early in 1608, someone held up for inspection two spectacle lenses. It is not known whether it was Lippershey or an employee who, while checking the lenses, by chance moved them into the same plane. Looking through the two pieces of glass, the holder was surprised by the magnification of the steeple on top of a church some distance away. Again focusing the pair of superimposed lenses, the man once more saw the steeple magnified.

Workmen, by turn, peered through the lenses, then stoically returned to their benches; but Lippershey's business sense alerted him to the commercial potential of the chance discovery. He made notes on the strength of the two lenses and, by letter, informed four friends of a lens arrangement which, when incorporated into an instrument, might enlarge and better define distant objects, improving natural vision.

On October 4, 1608, Lippershy applied to the Council of the Hague for exclusive rights to production of a two-lens instrument for viewing distant objects. His application was challenged by Zacharias Janssen (or Jansen), a neighbor and rival lensmaker; with witnesses to confirm his claim, Janssen said he had observed the double-lens phenomenon in 1590. Lippershey countered by demonstrating a metal tube with a lens at each end, evidence that as inventor of a *far-seeing eyeglass* he should have exclusive rights to its production. Janssen then introduced as evidence a similar tubular instrument.

Matters were further complicated by a petition to the Council made on October 17 by James Metius, of Alkmaar, also claiming to have invented a device for distant viewing. After due consideration of the three applications for exclusive production and sale of far-seeing eyeglasses, the Council awarded 900 florin to Lippershey, but withheld from him exclusive production rights.

Lippershey, Janssen and Metius all produced in their respective optical workshops a wide variety of far-seeing eyeglasses sold as curiosities to fascinated customers. Encyclopedias and other reference books variously credit the invention of the telescope to one, two, or even to all three of the Hollanders. Original records indicate that their contributions, all but simultaneous, were to the basic principle of the telescope, not to the development of a practical instrument.

The far-seeing eyeglass, much in vogue, was widely distributed in Europe immediately after the ruling by the Council of the Hague. There's a story, surely apocryphal, that a regal lady of the time purchased an eyeglass for the express purpose of spying on a husband noted for his dalliances in sylvan dells and along garden paths. A transaction of importance to the ultimate invention of a true telescope was the gift of one of Lippershey's far-seeing eyeglasses to Prince Maurice of Nassau, who recognized the gadget's potential for military reconnaissance.

It was the Prince's far-seeing eyeglass that came to the attention of Galileo, who made his claim as inventor of the telescope in *Il Saggiatore:* "What part belongs to me in the invention of the telescope, and why may I reasonably call it my own son? As I have long ago shown in my *Siderus*

Nuncius, news arrived at Venice, where I happened to be at the moment, that a Dutchman had presented to Prince Maurice of Nassau a glass with which one can see distant objects as clearly as though they were near. With this simple fact I returned to Padua, and, reflecting on the problem, I found a solution on the first night of my arrival home, and the next day I made the instrument and reported it to my friends at Venice. In the next six days I made a more perfect instrument with which I returned to Venice, and showed it for more than a month to the wonder and astonishment of the heads of the Republic."

Galileo is confirmed as the inventor of the true telescope by other seventeenth-century sources: scientific manuscripts, biographies, and correspondence to and from Galileo. His letters emphasize a pregnant phrase from *Il Saggiatore:* "with this simple fact." The far-seeing eyeglasses made in Holland were merely toys, objects providing pleasure for amazed owners. Galileo did not say he had seen the Dutch instrument in Venice, but more likely heard someone describe the principle of placing two lenses on a single plane, making a distant object appear to be close to the viewer.

The lenses superimposed by Galileo in a single day of experimentation did achieve the desired effect. In the instrument completed six days later, the distant object viewed was in an enlargement sixty times greater than that of the first. It was the second telescope that he took to Venice in August, 1609.

With an assurance common to many great scientists, Galileo wrote, "The beauty of my telescope is that it is so artlessly simple." And he was right. The telescope was constructed of a single metal tube. Galileo placed a convex lens in one end, and in the eyepiece at the other end, he placed a concave lens. A distant object seen through the eyepiece seemed to be immediately in front of the viewer. Rays of light emanating from the object struck the convex (bowed out) lens; the refracted (bent) light passed through the metal tube and struck the concave (bowed in) lens, magnifying the object in focus.

Within two weeks after his return from the demonstrations in Venice, Galileo had constructed a telescope capable of magnifying objects four hundred times. His knowledge of mathematics, lenses and the principles of light made it possible for Galileo to increase the size of images and extend the viewing distance. An avid astronomer, Galileo made telescopes powered to view the heavens, concentrating much of his research on studies of Jupiter and the moon.

Unable to hand-hold a telescope for viewing the planet Jupiter, Galileo mounted his instrument on an upright perpendicular support. With the telescope steady, Galileo was able to observe Jupiter, becoming the first man to see it in magnification. His fifth telescope, more powerful than the very first one he constructed, revealed the never-before-seen moon satellites revolving around Jupiter.

Through the same large telescope Galileo made the discovery that the "Milky Way is made up of millions of small stars, clustered brightly together." He noted the variable surface of the moon and verified his first observation by repeated experiments. Through ensuing years, Galileo described the valleys, plains and mountains on the moon which previously had been thought to be a flat-surfaced, round and shining ball.

Scientists now acknowledge Galileo's original studies as vital to exploration of the moon, the planet on which scientists of many nations concentrate their research. Ground-based scientists engaged in space-race projects want for their respective countrymen the honor of being the first earthlings to land on the lunar surface.

Galileo continued his astronomical research from the University of Florence, from which the professor's fame spread. Never in favor with scientists who held out for the status quo of established theories, Galileo incurred the displeasure of the Catholic Church by open concurrence with the theory of the universe propounded by Nicolaus Copernicus (1475–1543).

Copernicus, the Polish-born astronomer, by stating that the sun, not the planet earth, was the center of the universe, contradicted the then sacrosanct Aristotelian-Ptolemaic theory. The latter, placing man and his world, the earth, as the center of the universe, was blindly accepted by scientists and by the Church, which tolerated no challenge to the Principle of the Universe by Ptolemy (A.D. 127–151).

For the last thirty years of his life, Copernicus lived at Frauenberg, a little cathedral town not far from the Baltic coast. From a tower-room high on a hill, he made his astronomical observations, without the aid of a telescope. In detailed notes he described solar and lunar phenomena, the shapes of astral bodies and their movements as seen by the naked eye. A mathematical genius, he arrived at his astronomical conclusions by his own original and meticulous calculations.

It could not have escaped the attention of Galileo that

Copernicus, remote from a community of scholars, died a lonely man whose revolutionary contribution to science, the theory of the universe, was discredited by scientists and the Catholic hierarchy. But Galileo was not to be swayed by generally held opinions nor frightened by the consequences of dissent. He studied the writings of Copernicus and closely followed his mathematical deductions. In a letter of 1599, Galileo wrote: "Theories of Ptolemy and Copernicus are in direct conflict. So great is the separation that only one can be absolute. Because the heavens must certainly move in majestic order, someday someone, or perhaps many, must of certainty prove which theory is true and absolute."

Galileo built literally hundreds of telescopes, each an improvement on the one before, until he possessed instruments for scanning the skies that brought the "heavenly bodies directly into the room with me and makes it possible to observe, then mathematically chart the paths of those bodies." With his telescopes he viewed the sky at close range, often marveling at what Copernicus, as if by intuition, was able to envision. After long consideration and extensive research, Galileo was convinced of the correctness of the Copernican theory. Never one to back away from confrontation, he fearlessly stated, in speech and writing, why the Aristotelian-Ptolemaic theory was wrong.

He outraged scholars and the Church, placing both in delicate positions. The scientific community and the ruling factions in Italy basked in the glory reflected from the scientific contributions of Galileo. The Church was loath to threaten such a man with excommunication; its appeals for him to change his mind failed. Nor did threats move him from his conviction that the Ptolemaic theory was false.

In 1615 Galileo was denounced by the Church, but he continued to teach and to do astronomical research. On June 22, 1633, he was convicted of heresy and, under duress, signed a renunciation of the Copernican theory. In spite of that recantation, he was banished after a series of trials before religious tribunals and, in 1639, placed under house arrest.

From his home in the village of Arcetri, the gadfly of Italy continued to write about continuing research, actively carried out with one of his young pupils, Vincenzo Viviani. Even under house arrest, Galileo antagonized the Church, which refrained from further action because of the old man's reputation. Great international scholars made pilgrimages to Arcetri to honor or to consult with Galileo, who enjoyed the patronage and protection of men of power. Former students and other young men eager to learn from the master were at his side, even after he was bedridden.

Galileo extended the knowledge of the universe to such a dimension that men ever after were indebted to his genius. His world was ready for revolutionary ideas and theories. The transition from unquestioned beliefs was initiated a century earlier by Martin Luther, and unchallenged scientific theories by Copernicus and other farsighted scientists. Galileo not only made his own contributions but fired the imagination of students, of scientists and even of theologians. Scholars in universities, in religious communities and at royal courts were stimulated to delve into potential truths about man and his universe, searching for fact and challenging theory.

Galileo died in the early evening of January 8, 1642, his room piled with books and manuscripts. He received the last rites from a priest, but his funeral was modest, its service hardly befitting a man of his stature in the world of scholarship. For decades there was bitter controversy over his burial with its lack of honors. Viviani and others faithful to the memory of the great astronomer dared to face up to Pope Urban VIII and dissident members of the de Medici family. The Pope and his hierarchy, other churchmen, certain laymen and many moribund scientists, fearing the influence of Galileo even in death, tried in every way to prevent the perpetuation of his name and of his scientific accomplishments. Their lack of success is a matter of history.

AND AFTER

Isaac Newton, born the year Galileo died, often praised the contributions of the Italian astronomer. Newton admitted he might not have "seen the logical path of new conclusions in the realm of our universe" without the guidance of Galileo's research. Newton's reflecting telescope was a refinement of work begun in 1663 by a Scotsman, James Gregory. Gregory produced the first practical reflecting telescope, an instrument through which light, entering, strikes a reflecting mirror, and passes to the eyepiece lens where the image is concentrated and magnified.

With passing centuries, reflecting and refracting telescopes were steadily improved for precise use by scientific investigators probing deep into outer space. Methods of telescopic study were refined, revised, improvised; and new ones devised and tested.

The need for ever-larger reflecting telescopes was matched by the necessity to have mirrors of increasing diameters. The polishing and silver-coating of huge mirrors required procedures both so costly and problematical that scientists experimented with improvements. In 1935, Dr. John Strong, then professor of astrophysics at the California Institute of Technology, proposed the aluminum coating of mirrors, a technique that proved to be less expensive and more efficient than silver-coating. Silvered mirrors have to be recoated every few months; aluminum-coated mirrors function without servicing for as long as ten years.

Radiotelescopy evolved from the research of Grote Reber and of Karl G. Jansky of the Bell Telephone Laboratories. Jansky proved that the center of our galaxy powerfully emits electromagnetic radiation. He established that radio waves from celestial objects come from three major sources: thermal, gas in violent action, and radiation from cold neutral hydrogen in interstellar space.

The radio telescope depends for reception on a reflector. For this purpose Grote Reber constructed a dish antenna, thirty-one feet in diameter, to gather weak radio waves from outer space; these are brought to a receiver placed in the focus, and the record is then interpreted. The science of interpreting celestial radio waves gathered on a telescopic antenna has vastly increased scientific knowledge about the outer regions of the universe.

Telescopic investigation exemplifies the interdependence of inventions in scientific disciplines. Through powerful telescopes, scientists catch the beams of light from natural objects following predictable paths around the earth. Spectroscopic study of light received is made possible for astronomers and astrophysicists by the diffraction grating invented, in 1880, by Dr. Henry A. Rowland, late professor of physics at The Johns Hopkins University.

The invention makes possible the measurement of the light of chemical elements received in a spectroscope. Each element has the same coloration, the same spectral lines when light-giving conditions are identical; the atom of every known chemical emits several well-defined wavelengths of light, which in turn emit certain groups of colors.

The diffraction grating for measuring chemical content is a small, six-inch-long, rectangular piece of glass coated on one side to form a mirror surface. By means of an extremely sensitive machine, a diamond needle cuts 30,000 equidistant lines per square inch across the mirrored surface. When a beam of light strikes the surface of the mirror, the light is broken up, diffracted, into 100,000 different recordable colors by the 180,000 etched lines.

Light beamed through a spectroscope combined with a diffraction grating is diffracted into thousands of small color lines. These lines bounce back to a photographic plate where the colors, the spectral lines, are recorded. Specific combinations of colors indicate the presence of one specific chemical, or more.

By study of the spectral lines produced by light from an object in outer space, astrophysicists know what chemical elements are present in the astral body being studied. If they could receive light from Jupiter, which is not yet possible, they would know from its diffraction what chemical properties exist on that planet.

A deterrent to the chemical study of astral bodies is the murkiness of the earth's atmosphere through which light passes to the diffraction grating spectroscope-telescope. The investigator of the recorded spectral lines must try to sort those of the astral body from those of pollution in our atmosphere.

Dr. Strong, professor emeritus of astrophysics and physical meteorology at The Johns Hopkins University, attempted to eliminate the problem of "atmospheric garbage" by placing a telescope at the outer edges of our atmosphere. For a study of Venus and that planet's atmosphere, Dr. Strong, in cooperation with the U.S. Naval Research Institute, launched a manned balloon and gondola to a height where only two percent of the earth's atmosphere remained. A telescope designed by Dr. Strong was installed on top of the gondola. Light from the Venutian atmosphere, caught by the telescope, was beamed to a diffraction grating spectroscope within the balloon's sealed gondola. After the descent, Dr. Strong studied the spectral lines and was able to establish many facts about the long-controversial atmosphere of Venus, a brightly shining planet.

Scientists now find out about celestial objects from radio waves caught on a radio telescope and from light beams broken up by diffraction gratings. It is within the realm of probability that through high-powered telescopic devices man one day may actually see objects in outer space as clearly as he now sees his neighbors with his naked eye.

Inventive methods of microscopic study entitle a Dutch research expert to his high place in the history of science.

ANTON VAN LEEUWENHOEK
1632–1723, Dutch

In the hands of many seventeenth-century men, the microscope was a curiosity, a plaything like the far-seeing eyeglass, predecessor of the telescope. The invention of the microscope is attributed to Galileo Galilei in 1610 and to Zacharias Janssen of Middleburg, Holland, in 1590, the same year given for Janssen's observation of the magnification of distant objects by a far-seeing eyeglass. His long-delayed public statement about the telescopic property of his lens arrangement clouded the 1608 claim of his fellow townsman and business rival, Hans Lippershey, whose invention resulted from a chance superimposition of two lenses being inspected in his workshop.

Who is to know how many lensmakers of that day, when testing their optical products, also fortuitously produced a microscope? The simplest microscope is actually the magnifying glass, a single-lens device of short focal length, the focal length being the distance from the lens to the focus, or point of sharp image.

The magnifying glass, a basic instrument, became an extraordinary scientific tool for Anton van Leeuwenhoek, who, like numerous contemporaries of several countries, is also mistakenly credited with the invention of the microscope. Leeuwenhoek probably constructed more microscopes than any other experimenter of his age, and incontestably he did make greater contributions to microscopic research.

No one could possibly have predicted when Leeuwenhoek was young that he would go down in history as the originator and discoverer of several scientific disciplines. His ultimate achievements were made possible not by formal training but by his own nature: characteristics of curiosity, of patience, of persistence; physical qualities of superior eyesight and manual dexterity.

Anton, variously referred to as Antoni, Antonj, and even Antony, was born in Delft, Holland, on October 24, 1632. He was the son and grandson of basketmakers; their trade, no cottage craft of fashioning special baskets for individual customers, was a flourishing business dependent on exports of Delftware. The local pottery, famous and in demand around the world, was packed for safe shipment in baskets produced in the community.

When Anton was only eight, his widowed mother remarried and he went to live with relatives, in childhood attending small schools in two little Dutch towns. From age sixteen to twenty-two, he worked in Amsterdam as bookkeeper and cashier for a clothmaker. Whether Anton also became a trained draper, passing the trade's test, is a matter of biographical dispute; in any case, he was familiar with the examination of cloth with a magnifying glass. The glass was routinely used to inspect the quality of fibers and the regularity of weaving, the matching of patterns. Leeuwenhoek undoubtedly followed the same practice of inspection when, back in Delft and newly married in 1654, he became a retail merchant, dealing in cloth and haberdashery.

The following year, for no reason yet uncovered or known to biographers, Leeuwenhoek seriously began private study without the assistance of a teacher or tutor. Only poorly educated and not previously motivated to advanced learning, he must have had some goal in mind when he undertook such subjects as navigation, astronomy, mathematics and other sciences, including biology or, as it was then known, physics. In the light of his subsequent research, it was unfortunate that he did not study either Latin or English, both of which would have been of later benefit. As it was, he went through life knowing only his native tongue, neither reading nor speaking any other language.

A much respected citizen with a reputation for honesty and dependability, Leeuwenhoek concurrently held numerous official posts in Delft. He was appointed sheriff's chamberlain in 1660, general district supervisor in 1677 and, in 1679, wine-gauger. That position was probably given to him because he had passed a land surveyor's examination in 1669, both activities being dependent on measurements of one kind and another.

Leeuwenhoek's private life was not without its sorrow. His first wife died in 1666, and he married again in 1671, his second wife living for twenty-four years. Of six children, the only one who survived childhood was Maria, spinster daughter of the first marriage and her father's lifetime devoted companion.

Each of Leeuwenhoek's public positions carried with it a modest stipend, and not all made heavy demands on his time. Even so, he complained in letters that the multiplicity of his duties cut into the hours he wanted to spend with his microscopes. He was all but sixty-seven when, as chamberlain, he was given an official assistant; his assistant winegauger was not appointed until 1704.

Leeuwenhoek's energy and capacity for hard work must have been boundless because, by 1673, he was so well known for the quality of his instruments and for the successes of his "observations" that his work was commended to the Royal Society, which had received its royal charter in 1662. Members of the Royal Society of London for the Improving of Natural Knowledge were scholarly and, for the most part, young men who encouraged correspondence from others with equally inquiring minds. The correspondent who introduced Leeuwenhoek to the Royal Society was Reinier de Graaf, a physician of Delft whose own research was in medicine, specifically in anatomy.

The letter from de Graaf conclusively proves that Leeuwenhoek was not the inventor of the microscopes: ". . . I am writing to tell you that a certain most ingenious person here, named Leeuwenhoek, has devised microscopes which far surpass those which we have hitherto seen, manufactured by Eustachio Divini and others. The enclosed letter from him [Leeuwenhoek], wherein he describes certain things which he has observed more accurately than previous authors, will afford you a sample of his work; and if it please you and you would test the skill of this most diligent man and give him encouragement, then pray send him a letter containing your suggestions, and proposing to him more difficult problems of the same kind."

In Leeuwenhoek's "enclosed letter," he described observations of mold, the bee and the water-louse, sufficiently interesting the Royal Society that Secretary Oldenburg requested the Dutch investigator to send more drawings and further notes on his observations. There was to follow almost half a century of close association between Leeuwenhoek and the Royal Society.

His first letter indicated that he knew the work of Robert Hooke, whose *Micrographia,* in 1665, was the first book on microscopy. Leeuwenhoek could study the drawings but, unable to read the text, must have had at least parts of the book translated. Hooke, who became curator of experiments of the Royal Society in 1662, was a mathematician, inventor, physician and, like Leeuwenhoek, also a surveyor. In his *Micrographia,* Hooke described cells in plant tissue observed through his compound microscope.

The compound microscope was not to be perfected for about two hundred years, and observation through seventeenth-century models was far from satisfactory. A compound microscope is made of at least two double-convex lenses: the lower lens is the objective, and the upper lens, at the opposite end of the hollow cylinder, is the eyepiece. In great simplification of the principle, the object on which the instrument is focused is magnified by the lower lens and its resultingly enlarged image is magnified by the upper lens.

The simple glass lenses available for seventeenth-century microscopes had two major faults: They gave a curve to straight lines at the margin of the field of view, and tinged with blue and yellow the edge of the object being studied, whatever its natural color. The errors inherent in the simple lens were multiplied in a complex microscope. Leeuwenhoek, in order to circumvent the problems, used single-lens devices of high magnification. Magnification is expressed in diameters; for example, a magnification five times greater than the object is known as five diameter, or 5X. Some of the more than four hundred lenses ground by Leeuwenhoek were 270X. At that magnification, the single-lens microscope had its own limitation: a small field of observation. The higher the magnification, the greater the curvature of the lens, and the smaller the distortion-free field.

Twenty-six of Leeuwenhoek's microscopes were willed to the Royal Society, and detailed descriptions were published, stressing the simplicity of the design, the complexity of the preparation of materials to be observed: ". . . for the construction of these instruments, it is the same in them all, and the Apparatus is very simple and convenient. They are all single Microscopes, consisting of a very small double-convex glass, let into a socket, between two silver plates riveted together and pierced with a small hole. The object is placed on a silver point, or needle, which, by means of screws of the same metal, provided for that purpose, may be turned about, raised or depressed, and brought nearer or farther from the glass, as the eye of the observer, the nature of the object, and the convenient examination of its several parts may require.

"Mr. Leeuwenhoek fixed his objects, if they were solid, to this silver point, with glew [glue]; and when they were fluid, or of such a nature as not to be commodiously viewed unless spread on glass, he first fitted them on a little plate of talc, or excessively thin-blown glass, which he afterwards glewed to the needle, in the same manner as his other objects. . . . The glasses are all exceedingly clear, and shew [show] the object very bright and distinct, which must be owing to the great care this Gentleman took in the choice of his glass, his exactness in giving it the true figure; and afterwards, amongst many, reserving such only for his use, as he, upon trial, found to be most excellent. Their powers of magnifying are different, as different sorts of objects may require; and, as on the one hand, being all ground glasses, none of them are so small, and consequently magnify to so great a degree as some of those drops, frequently used in other microscopes; yet, on the other, the distinctness of these very much exceeds what I have met with in glasses of that sort."

Whether Leeuwenhoek bequeathed what he thought to be his best microscopes to the Royal Society may never be known. Those disappeared, and only ten of his microscopes are known to exist today. The number he reputedly made varies, depending on the source, from less than four hundred to more than five hundred. How many he produced cannot be estimated with any degree of accuracy because he admittedly had instruments through which no one else was permitted to look. Those he kept hidden away along with numerous microscopes which had special lenses ground for specific kinds of research. Certain microscopes were made available to scholarly visitors for whom Leeuwenhoek set up demonstrations of the most elementary order.

He did not share his method of dark-field illumination, a way of viewing brightly lighted objects against a dark background. He wrote about seeing blood globules (cells) as clearly as if they were sandgrains on a "piece of black taffety silk," which surely suggests a dark background. Scientists familiar with Leeuwenhoek's experiments speculated on his method of lighting, their opinions divergent for lack of information from him.

Leeuwenhoek did his research and studies at a period when measurement was of prime importance to the development of exact natural science. Other investigators in many countries, inspired by the example of Galileo, were meticulously recording the measurements of disparate research projects. Leeuwenhoek, as the first man to measure microscopic objects, was the originator of micrometry.

Both logical and methodical, he chose as standards for comparisons common measurements and familiar objects. He had a five-inch brass rule, marked off with thirty subdivisions for an inch. A coarse grain of sand was a comparative object because he found it to be one thirtieth of an inch in diameter. A hair from his wig was the guide for how many hairbreadths there were to an inch. He also used a counter of sorts to estimate the numbers of microorganisms in a sample sucked up into a small tube.

It has been erroneously suggested that Leeuwenhoek's experience as a wine-gauger prepared him for making exact measurements of microscopic objects. In fact, he initiated the discipline of bacteriology by the history-making discovery of protozoa in 1654, five years before he became wine-gauger. The need for precision was the only thing common to his microscopic measurements and the barrel measurements, about which it was much easier to be precise. Leeuwenhoek's official functions as wine-gauger were to inspect weights and measures, to check the volume of oil and wine barrels, and, by law, to gauge personally every barrel filled for the first time in Delft.

Protozoa, low forms of life, chiefly single-cell and mostly aquatic, were discovered by Leeuwenhoek in a water sample from a local inland lake. *Animalcules* was what he called the microorganisms in his glass vial, and he described various others besides protozoa, noting the colors, the shapes, the motions and relative sizes, an elementary first attempt at giving some sort of measurement to the objects viewed through his microscope.

On October 9, 1676, Leeuwenhoek wrote a much-quoted and long-famous letter about his studies of little animals that were "to my eye, more than 10,000 times smaller than the animalcule . . . called by the name water-flea or water-louse." He referred to an organism, probably *Daphnia,* which is visible without the aid of any magnifying lens. The magnification of the microscope through which the organisms "10,000 times smaller" were viewed is not known, but through it Leeuwenhoek made incredible observations of the structure and actions of the objects.

After studying animalcules contained in the water of a rain tub, Leeuwenhoek set up successive experiments with rain, well, sea and snow water. Having earlier theorized about the difference in the taste of sugar and salt, he wanted to know what caused the "pungency of *Pepper* upon our tongue." He made an infusion of pepper in snow water and found in it three kinds of protozoa, and a fourth type of animalcule that microbiologists accept as having been unmistakably bacteria. While satisfying his insatiable curiosity about all substances, Leeuwenhoek was opening up a new field of science. His own comment on the research was: "These observations concerning living creatures in the above mentioned liquids require indeed closer attention and description, but that whole also requires a whole man which my circumstances do not allow of, and I have employed only my spare time upon them."

However difficult it was for Leeuwenhoek to make his observations, he wrote detailed notes of experiments that might be carried out by members of the Royal Society to whom he sent his letter-reports. Although several attempts to see the animalcules in a pepper infusion failed in London, the experiments were repeated until Hooke confirmed the Dutch investigator's findings. A number of reasons may account for the necessity of doing the studies over and over again before a successful observation was achieved. Leeuwenhoek may well have experienced some original failures. His colleagues in Holland and in England credited him with keener eyesight than most men. He used with skill and imagination microscopes he ground for his own special purposes. No one else had access to such precise and specialized viewing lenses, for he frankly stated, "My method for seeing the very smallest animalcules . . . I do not impart to others, nor yet that for seeing many animalcules at once, but I keep that for myself alone."

Robert Hooke was Secretary of the Royal Society when Leeuwenhoek was unanimously made a Fellow, an honor that surprised and delighted him; he was also touched by the fact that the certificate was worded in Dutch, not the customary Latin. He received an occasional member of the Society in Delft, but never traveled to England, correspondence being his chief contact with the Society, to which he contributed much in knowledge and prestige. The members respected his judgment, knowing him to be modest in his claims and quick to acknowledge some error in initial experiments. He often corrected his own mistakes before they were pointed out by others, and was open-minded to criticism of a method or a conclusion.

Unlike some investigators of the same time, Leeuwenhoek did not theorize in writing without stating that he was doing so. His notes of observations were factual, and his drawings remarkable for a man of absolutely no training. He drew what he saw with an accuracy that, in some cases, has been confirmed by modern photomicrography; many of his drawings were copied by a skilled artist, whose sketches were then sent out with the scientific report-letters.

Leeuwenhoek's drawings of bacteria in tartar of the mouth might be an inspiration for advertising artists today when oral hygiene is so much publicized. He described in a letter of September, 1683, his own method of dental care: "I am in the habit of rubbing my teeth in the morning, and then swill out my mouth with water; and often after eating, to clean my back teeth with a toothpick, as well as rubbing them hard with a cloth, wherefore my teeth back and front remain as clean and white that only a few people of my age (fifty-one) can compare with me. Also when I rub my gums with hard salt, they will not bleed. Yet all this does not make my teeth so clean but that I can see, looking at them with a hollow mirror, that something will stick and grow between some of the molars and teeth, a little white matter, as thick as batter. Observing it I judged that although I could not see anything moving in it there were yet living animalcules in it. I then mixed it several times with pure rain-water, in which there were no animalcules, and also with saliva that I took from my mouth after eliminating the air bubbles lest these should stir the spittle. I then again and again saw that there were many small living animalcules in the said matter, which moved very prettily."

He described four different bacteria and the continued research with tartar from the mouths of other people, young and old, male and female. He found an "incredible number of living animalcules swimming more nimbly than I had ever seen up to this time" in tartar from an abstemious old man who admitted to never having cleaned his mouth. A similar activity of bacteria was present in tartar from another man whose teeth had never been cleaned, but whose consumption of alcohol and use of tobacco were heavy. Leeuwenhoek remarked that "such a stench comes from the mouth of many that one can hardly bear talking to them. Many call this a stenching breath, but actually it is in most cases a stinking mouth."

Leeuwenhoek prepared his experiments as scientifically as if he had been trained in laboratory techniques. "Pure rain-water" was the basis for many of his infusions; specimens were clearly labeled; equipment was always scrubbed clean and often sterilized; the microscopes were kept in constant repair, the hinges oiled, the lenses polished. In his description of one specific research project, the famous microscopist stated that a certain piece of equipment was a china dish which had not been contaminated by food for a decade.

His procedures made possible the wide range of his observations and examinations, and the broad scope of his discoveries and conclusions. Through his microscopes he discovered: The spermatozoa in human semen. *Hydra,* the fresh-water polyp that, four decades later, was to be the subject of definitive scientific study. The capillaries, confirm-

ing the observations of Marcello Malpighi, and further adding to Harvey's theory of blood circulation expounded more
than a half a century earlier. Parthenogenesis, the development within virgin females of eggs unfertilized by male
sperm. Aphids were the organisms studied by Leeuwenhoek.

Having originated a new theory of generation, Leeuwenhoek sought similarities in the reproductive processes of animals and plants. His extensive botanical experiments particularly stressed propagation and the presence and function of
seeds; he even suggested what today is called hybridization.
While doing in-depth studies of the structure of wood,
Leeuwenhoek examined many kinds of trees.

In the field of medicine, he added to the knowledge of
histology through his examination of animal tissues, and
studied not only flesh fibers and muscles but teeth, hair and
bone. The eye was an organ of the body that early interested
him, as evidenced by his first letter to the Royal Society,
that report including details about his observations of the
eye of the bee.

When possible in medical and other studies, Leeuwenhoek tried to find practical applications of the knowledge
gained. Because the weevil was an economic hazard, damag-
ing to corn supplies and to flour for baking, Leeuwenhoek
gave time and thought to the propagation of that "very noxi-
ous insect." Other subjects of his entomological research
were the fly, the flea, the spider, the ant, moths and numerous other insects of varying sizes, many microscopic.

In de Graaf's letter of introduction to the Royal Society,
he suggested that "more difficult problems" be posed for
Leeuwenhoek. That was never necessary because letter-
reports of his new theories, original ideas and startling dis-

coveries flowed steadily from Holland to England. Inventiveness and an imaginative approach to studies with the microscope kept Leeuwenhoek way ahead of other investigators in both ideas and projects.

As his fame increased, he had more visitors than he could receive; in one four-day period there were more than twenty-six callers with letters of introduction, and one baron and an earl, neither with credentials. Leeuwenhoek's one regret for many years was that there was, in Delft, no one with whom he could share his exciting experiences with the scientific tool that so absorbed and fascinated him—the single-lens microscope.

AND AFTER

Today's research microscope, in all its extraordinary variations and complexities, bears as little relationship to the single-lens microscope as the Montgolfier balloon to the manned space capsule. Sophisticated power sources expose, with rays and beams and impulses, the structure, motion and distribution of phenomena that can only be designated as infinitesimal particles—molecular, cellular and subcellular. The phase-contrast microscope reveals invisible objects of the same density but of different optical paths; the ultramicroscope, the scattering of particles in waves or beams; the ion microscope, the pattern of a metal, including the material's atomic structure.

In the 1930's, a team of German scientists developed a microscope dependent for operation on beams of electrons, not on light waves. A practical electron microscope, portable and relatively inexpensive, was developed at the Radio Corporation of America laboratories by Dr. V. K. Zworykin. Successful in operation by 1942, the RCA electron microscope raised the magnification of the object being studied to 100,000X.

The limit of capability of the electron microscope and of other intricate microscopes, existent and in development, is in the mind of man. Unknown and unpredictable future studies are dependent on modern men with imagination and creativity comparable to that of Leeuwenhoek, who, in accomplishment, transcended the single-lens microscope, an instrument primitive by today's standards.

Watt advanced steam power, which was to the industrial revolution what atomic energy is to today's economy.

JAMES WATT
1736–1819, Scottish

No one can be blamed for saying James Watt invented the steam engine because that false claim is even now to be found in print. The truth, that Watt produced the first practical and efficient steam engine, is a misleading understatement unfair to him. He was a creative inventor, a precise mechanical draftsman, and an imaginative theorist whose many achievements broke through technical and technological barriers existing in the late eighteenth and early nineteenth centuries. Watt not only showed originality in the design of his steam engine and its components but opened the way for such twentieth-century scientific disciplines as cybernetics and thermodynamics.

A persistent anecdote about Watt's being inspired to invention by the sight of steam issuing from the spout of a tea kettle in the family kitchen is impossible to substantiate. Like the legend of Newton and the apple, the oft-repeated story of an aunt reprimanding little James for wasting his time doing tricks with steam from a kettle must be recognized as apocryphal.

It is undeniable that Watt, by inheritance and through the

misfortune of childhood illness, was prepared for his ultimate career and scientific inventions. At six, he amused himself by doing geometric drawings to illustrate simple problems of mathematics, a subject much talked about in the family; several relatives, including a grandfather, were mathematicians by profession. James's dexterity was inherited from his father, a carpenter by trade and training, who progressed in business to house construction, shipbuilding and, later, general merchandising. The senior Watt helped James to set up an attic workshop when the child, in poor health, could not start to school with those of his age group. Using a set of small tools made especially for him, the sickly youngster showed marked aptitude for working with his hands.

The little boy, unable to attend formal classes, learned techniques and methods from carpenters employed by his father. On the waterfront of his hometown, Greenock, Scotland, James watched the operation of mechanical devices essential to the shipping industry. In the wheelhouse of many a vessel, he observed the replacement of navigational instruments which had been repaired in his father's shop. In his own little workroom, the child built numerous gadgets and models, including a loading crane, a pulley, capstan, pump, and even a barrel organ.

When James eventually attended school, he was a competent student but not a convivial schoolmate, being introspective and far from robust. After graduation he could not work toward a university degree because family business reverses made it necessary for him to be self-supporting at seventeen. Determined to be an instrument-maker, he was unwilling to enter into an apprenticeship of several years duration. In London, then the center for the training of those in the trade he chose, he paid for the privilege of learning, and also worked in his master's shop without salary. At the end of an exhausting twelve months, Watt returned to Scotland where he was engaged by administrators of the University of Glasgow as their official mathematical instrument-maker. He was given lodging on campus and a shop there.

Glasgow craftsmen's guilds may have kept Watt from establishing a town shop as he originally intended. Whatever the reason for his association with the university, it was of prime importance to the future of Watt and of steam power. His creative thinking on the subject was crystallized by a difficult task to which he was assigned: the restoration of a model of the steam engine invented in the early eighteenth century by Thomas Newcomen. Qualified by mechanical experience and theoretical study for the repair of the malfunctioning model, Watt went beyond its challenge to design his own steam engine.

He was established, if by chance, in an environment dominated by a vigorous faculty of young intellectuals dedicated to science. Professors and students alike were attracted to his shop, filling it with the ferment of their ideas and enjoying in it the opportunity to experiment with and examine the instruments he made and repaired. A congenial group regularly gathered in his living quarters to discuss scholarly problems and advance theories on a wide range of subjects pertinent to the industrial developments and scientific upsurge of their day.

After six years of living on campus, Watt left it to take lodging in town where, at last, he was able to have a second shop, extending his work to the making of a wider variety of instruments, including musical ones. His duties and personal contacts at the two shops and at the university daily increased Watt's knowledge of physical science, then known as natural philosophy. Through association and by application, he acquired a sound, if informal, education in science by learning physics, chemistry and, of course, ever more mathematics.

Two close friends of Watt's were Joseph Black, chairman of the department of anatomy and lecturer on chemistry at the university, and John Robison, a student of remarkable ability. Black, eight years older than Watt, was an eminent scholar gifted in experimentation, particularly in calorimetry, measurement of heat. Watt always acknowledged the influence and advice of Black, in both the early years of their association and throughout their lives. Black found Watt to be possessed of "most uncommon talents for mechanical knowledge and practice."

Robison, three years younger than Watt, had a rare talent for imaginative speculation, and theorized in his student days about the ultimate uses of steam power for operating weaving looms and for moving the wheels of carriages and other vehicles. On completion of his studies, he adventured throughout the world on numerous missions. Returning as lecturer in chemistry at the university, taking Black's place, Robison was ever the informal consultant to Watt on mathematics and other subjects of their mutual interest. Respectful of Watt's capabilities, Robison said of him, ". . . everything became science to his hands."

Watt's metamorphosis from master craftsman to scientist-inventor dated from the winter of 1763–1764 when he was asked to overhaul the Newcomen steam engine model belonging to the University of Glasgow. The model, faulty in operation, had been returned from London where a famous instrument-maker admitted to his lack of success in the attempt at repair. After examination of the model, Watt first worked, according to his own statement, "as a mere mechanician, but then began to study it seriously."

In his spare time Watt read reports by early designers of engines, even doing specific test experiments. He examined the inventions of Denis Papin and of Thomas Savery. Papin designed a digester that operated on the principle of the modern pressure cooker, and a crude engine so poorly constructed that it unfortunately failed to achieve its considerable potential. In 1678, Thomas Savery designed the first steam engine with separate vessels for steam and water, a device consisting of a boiler to produce steam and a vessel for condensing steam by cooling. The engine was not strong enough for the uses anticipated by Slavery: to provide water for cities and towns; to operate mills; to drain mines, preventing floods deep underground. Although Savery was disappointed by the limitations of his engine, it was the first to supply water for mansions.

Mine drainage and large-scale water supply operations were the concern of any number of inventors working at the turn of the eighteenth century. Designs for and theories about "fire engines" for pumping water to prevent mine flooding and to supply water for home consumption were rife at the beginning of the industrial revolution. A contemporary of Savery's, Thomas Newcomen, and the latter's

assistant, John Calley, were both craftsmen capable of transferring Newcomen's designs from drawing board to models
and to operate machines.

Newcomen invented an atmospheric engine with a driving
force dependent on the opposition of atmospheric pressure
to the vacuum created by steam condensation. A piston was
put to work in his condenser-cylinder; a fit, both airtight and
steamtight, was assured by leather or rope packing. The
packing was sealed by a small layer of water at the upper
side. The steam condensation was effected by injection of a
cold water spray into the steam cylinder; previously, steam
vessels were cooled slowly and naturally, or faster by an
external spray. Newcomen and others improved his steam
engine which, while workable, was costly to construct and to
operate. It was the engine most used for more than half a
century, from 1711 until Watt advanced steam power by his
inventive and original designs.

In theory, Watt understood the Newcomen engine; but
when he began the repair of the model, he carefully studied
the design and experimented with the operation. The engine,
supposed to be a scale model, did not function properly even
when all moving parts were in working order. Strong fire
under the boiler made the engine perform only a "few
strokes" before stopping. At least in the model, the quantities of steam and fuel consumed seemed to be out of all
reasonable and direct proportion to the energy produced.

Minor changes slightly increased the efficiency of the
model, but Watt recognized a basic design fault in any engine so wasteful of steam and heat. He examined the principles and mechanisms, considering the suitability of materials and the properties of steam as a source of power. His

scientific approach, unique to his day, was in the best tradition of engineering, burgeoning as a profession.

Watt himself credited the inventor John Smeaton with having started the profession of engineering, saying, ". . . he made engineers of us all." Smeaton, a careful craftsman like Watt, also was first employed as a mathematical instrument-maker. Innumerable improvements of the Newcomen engine issued from Smeaton's shop, where he tried devices of his own design on an experimental steam engine model. He eventually earned an international reputation as a consultant on pumping machinery and as a construction engineer.

When Watt began research similar to Smeaton's, he did undoubtedly use a tea kettle, heating the water with a candle under it. "A glass tube was bent at right-angles; one end was inserted horizontally into the spout of a tea kettle and the other was immersed perpendicularly in well-water contained in a cylindrical glass vessel, and steam was made to pass through it until it ceased to be condensed and the water in the glass vessel was become nearly boiling hot. The water in the glass vessel was then found to have gained an addition of about one-sixth part from the condensed steam. Consequently water converted into steam can heat about six times its own weight of well-water to 212°, or till it can condense no more steam."

The theory of latent heat, stressing the higher amount of heat in steam than in hot water, or in vapor than in liquid, was earlier discovered by Joseph Black, to whom Watt turned for clarification of his elementary test. After Black's confirmation of the accuracy of Watt's findings, the latter full understood the heat loss of Newcomen's engine, which had steam changing to water within a single cylinder. He saw that two separate containers were essential if the cylinder was to be "maintained always as hot as the steam which entered it."

In his old age, Watt told about the May day, in 1765, when the principle of his own steam engine became clear to him:

"It was in the Green of Glasgow, I had gone to take a walk on a fine Sabbath afternoon. I had entered the Green by the gate at the foot of Charlotte Street—had passed to the old washing-house. I was thinking upon the engine at the time, and had gone so far as the Herd's house when the idea came into my mind that, as steam is an elastic body, it would rush into a vacuum, and if communication were made between the cylinder and an exhausted vessel, it would rush into it, and might there be condensed without cooling the cylinder. I then saw that I must get quit of the condensed steam and injection water, if I used a jet as in Newcomen's engine. Two ways of doing this occurred to me: first, the water might be run off by a descending pipe, if an offlet could be got at the depth of 35 or 36 feet, and any air might be extracted by a small pump: the second was to make the pump large enough to extract both water and air. . . . I had not walked further than the Golf House when the whole thing was arranged in my mind."

He immediately made a scale model designed to work at relatively low steam pressure. The engine was literally to be steam driven in contrast to Newcomen's engine, which was dependent on atmospheric pressure against a vacuum produced by steam. Watt first patented an engine in 1769, but it was to be seven years before he settled to serious work on it, and three more before it was put to industrial use. Disappointment and even despondency marked the way to the engine he so optimistically planned:

"My method of lessening the consumption of the steam and consequently fuel, in fire-engines, consists of the following principles:—

"*First*, that the vessel in which the powers of steam are to be employed to work the engine—which is called the cylinder in common fire-engines, and which I call the steam vessel—must, during the whole time the engine is at work, be kept hot as the steam that enters it; first, by enclosing it in a case of wood or any other materials that transmit heat slowly; secondly, by surrounding it with steam or other heated bodies; and thirdly, by suffering neither water nor any other substance colder than the steam to enter or touch it during that time.

"*Secondly*, in engines that are to be worked, wholly or partially, by condensation of steam, the steam is to be condensed in vessels distinct from the steam vessel or cylinder, though occasionally communicating with them. These vessels I call 'condensers'; and while the engines are working these condensers ought at least to be kept as cold as the air in the neighborhood of the engines, by the application of water or other cold bodies.

"*Thirdly*, whatever air or other elastic vapor is not condensed by the cold of the condenser, and may impede the working of the engine, is to be drawn out of the steam vessels or condensers by means of pumps, wrought by the engines themselves or otherwise.

"*Fourthly*, I intend in many cases to employ the expansive force of steam to press on the pistons, or whatever may be used instead of them, in the same manner as the pressure of the atmosphere is now employed in common fire-engines. In cases where cold water cannot be had in plenty, the engines may be wrought by this force of steam only, by discharging the steam into the open air after it has done its office."

He continued his specifications by speaking of the potential of a rotary engine, and also stating that, in some cases, he intended to "apply a degree of cold not capable of reducing the steam to water, but of contracting it considerably," for working the engine by alternate expansion and contraction of steam. In conclusion, he suggested oils, wax, resin, and animal fats among other substances for making pistons and other engine parts steamtight.

Financial backing for the building of the first engine was provided by Dr. John Roebuck, founder of the Carron Iron Works, near Edinburgh, who was introduced to Watt by Black. The business association of Roebuck and the inventor was not as rewarding for either of them as their lifetime friendship. The wealthy Dr. Roebuck, knowledgeable and understanding about science, unfortunately suffered business setbacks that necessitated a reduction of funds for the construction of Watt's working engine model. Watt, in turn, beset by personal debts, became a surveyor and builder of canals, giving only his spare time to steam engine experimentation.

By nature a procrastinator, Watt labored too long over the engine design and the execution of its mechanical parts, and on the assemblage. He knew himself to be too precise, cautious and painstaking, but was unable to correct his recognized and admitted fault. Work delay also was caused by various ailments which then continued to plague him; his physical condition was improved by his outdoor work with canal projects and, by middle age, he enjoyed good health for the first time in his life.

Watt's first working scale-model engine was set up in a building near Dr. Roebuck's home in the early summer of 1769. In September the engine was run through a series of tests that did not satisfy the inventor. Watt's reservations about the engine were balanced by a hope for ultimate corrections: "The boiler with a small fire easily supplied more steam than we could destroy, although there were many outlets (flues) for it, which we took no care to stop, being employed otherwise. The boiler-top and wooden cylinder were very tight, as were all our vacuum joints and valves: the plates that let out steam were at the man-hole door and at the screws that fastened the steambox to the wooden cylinder, which, had other things been right, we should soon have corrected."

Things were not soon corrected. Nor was the way ahead smooth for Watt until May, 1774, when he moved to Birmingham, England, and became the partner of Matthew Boulton, a successful industrialist. The firm of Boulton and Watt first prospered, then faltered in a general depression, and afterward boomed. Later it was distinguished as a second-generation business managed by sons of the original partners.

In his large Soho factory close to Birmingham, Matthew Boulton employed six hundred workmen for the manufacture of several products. He inherited his father's original business of stamping and piercing silver and immediately expanded operations, introducing modern methods of production and unique labor relations. He traveled widely in the British Isles, investigating the latest scientific inventions and procedures and buying well-designed tools. His representatives, dispatched to the Continent, searched for products that might be mass-produced. Boulton's Soho factory was powered by water raised from a stream dam by waterwheel, a system he knew to be inefficient. His interest in the potential of steam power for manufacturing purposes considerably antedated his partnership with Watt.

The formal partnership of Boulton and Watt was dated June 1, 1775, and the patent of Watt, extended to 1800, gave him rights in Great Britain and her colonies. By private arrangement, Boulton received two thirds of the patent rights, paying the full expenses of manufacturing and a salary of three hundred pounds a year to Watt.

At the Soho plant, Watt went forward with the production of an engine, many parts of which had been in his mind since the long-remembered Sunday of 1765. His single-action engine, perfected in 1774, featured three separate components: a boiler, a condenser and the cylinder. The closed-top cylinder and piston were kept hot by steam passing through an admission pipe from the boiler. The cylinder's lower end opened to the condenser.

Three valves controlled the operation: An exhaust valve, opening at the beginning of the downstroke, produced a vacuum below the piston. Simultaneously a steam valve admitted steam above the piston. Steam and exhaust valves closed at the end of the downstroke. The equilibrium valve, opening at the completion of the downstroke, equalized steam and pressure on both sides of the piston. A heavy pump rod, or counterpoise, drove the engine beam to its side

and the piston up within the cylinder. Automatically functioning valves continued the operation. Watt's air pump
forced condensed water from the condenser into a hot well,
from which the feed pump raised it to the boiler for re-
circulation. The condenser, the closed cylinder and the air
pump were the first devices to establish him as an ingenious
inventor.

Watt, with his characteristic reluctance to let go of a
project, wanted to continue with experimentation and, as
adviser, with the design of engines for specific locations.
Boulton, more realistic, pushed for the production and sale
of engines. Watt wrote from Soho to his father, "The fire-
engine I have invented is now going, and answers much
better than any other that has yet been made." Prospective
customers agreed and placed orders with the firm.

By partnership agreement, Watt had to oversee the manufacture of the engines but, freed from financial worries,
found time also for experiments and inventions. In 1871 he
took out a patent for a double-acting steam engine with
many practical and very advanced devices. His steam chest
and slide valve admitted steam alternately to opposite sides
of the piston. It operated with an upstroke and downstroke
within a cylinder closed at both ends. The cutoff, first set at
one quarter of a stroke, was shortly reduced to a fraction of a
stroke. Preliminary to the cutoff decision, Watt experimented with an indicator diagram, a graph of steam pressure changes during the stroke. A refinement of the device is
today known as the Watt indicator. The automatic timing of
admission of steam and of cutoff is done by the slide valve
housed in the steam chest.

Wood for heating boiler water was as impractical as the

waterwheel for supplying water, and soon coal became the heat-source fuel. The very substance that the Watt engine was instrumental in bringing up from the mines was burned in great quantities at the Boulton and Watt factory for its coal-gas lighting. That form of illumination was invented by William Murdock, a trusted and prized employee of the firm, who was also its longtime representative in Cornwall, where the Watt engine was installed in many mines. The miners did not like the meters Watt invented to record the amount of work done by an engine. The automatic monitoring system annoyed the engine operators who, previous to the installation of the meters, arbitrarily stopped an engine for the eighteenth-century counterpart of the coffee break.

Intent on constant improvements of his pumping machines, Watt long resisted Boulton's urgings for the design of a rotative engine. When, under pressure from his partner, Watt finally put his mind to an engine capable of operating plant machinery in factories, he was irritated to find that a more progressive inventor had patented the crank. Watt considered it to be in the public domain, as it had been in use for centuries, especially to turn a potter's wheel. He invented the flywheel as an adjunct for the crank of the reciprocating engine with its rotary motion and a governor to keep the engine's motion steady, even during alteration of its load.

No better proof of the importance of the rotative engine is needed than the statistics from the Boulton and Watt records. The firm, in a twenty-five-year period, produced more than five-hundred engines: one third for pumping and two thirds for rotation of manufacturing machinery. Royalty on the rotative engines was based on equivalent production by the draft horses necessary to do the required job. Watt is credited with having established the term "horsepower." The horsepower of his engines, while one hundred times less than that now attainable in power plants, more than doubled the work of horses. The *watt,* an electrical measure of modern power, was named in honor of the inventor.

With his fanaticism about fine workmanship, Watt improved inventions when they interested him. Many of his inventive ideas were not realized because he did not choose to carry forward with them. One was the design of a computing machine which, like the steam governor, was in the concept of twentieth-century automation and cybernetics. His indicator, mechanically attached to the cylinder to produce an automatic record of steam pressure, was a pioneer device, leading to the science of thermodynamics.

Watt instituted the field of office machinery with a copying device he invented to facilitate his paper work. It was to be another century before the invention of the typewriter, which added to the speed of office correspondence and record-keeping. For fun, Watt even made copies of letters from his wife and friends. His consistent use of the copy machine made available, for posterity, records, letters and notes important to historians of the industrial revolution and to biographers of its leaders.

The contributions of Watt in numbers and importance of his inventions are immeasurable, particularly in regard to steam power. Without his creativity and mechanical ability, its potential would have been long delayed. His limitation was lack of vision for the immediate future. He foresaw that, in ensuing centuries, steam power would radically change industrial production, but steadfastly refused to experiment with the use of steam power for locomotion. While still on the campus of the University of Glasgow, he knew of Robison's prediction of the steam operation of vehicles, but did not pursue the subject. Years later, Watt, still uninterested in transportation, dissuaded Murdock from patenting a steam locomotive design. To the end, Watt's engines were stationary.

AND AFTER

Richard Trevithick (1771–1833) dared to enter the fiield of locomotion disregarded by the cautious and more knowledgeable Watt. The two men knew each other because Trevithick was, like his father, a foreman in a Cornwall mine that depended on the steam engine for operation. The Cornish miner experimented with steam-engine boilers, eventually making workable ones, but not before several had exploded from high-pressure imperfections. Watt disapproved of the impatient Trevithick, who lacked the scientific background and the technical skills necessary to building mechanically precise engines.

In 1800, Trevithick invented a high-pressure steam engine which was actually a horseless carriage, the forerunner of the automobile, not the locomotive. Trevithick's first self-propelled carriage even looked like an automobile, the driver sitting on a platform at the front of the coach body. Rear wheels, ten feet in diameter, moved independently, not together. Small front wheels that turned on an axis were steered by a handlebar. There were gears for changes of speed, a brake, and an automatic blower. The firebox at the rear of the vehicle housed the cylinders.

Moving at the rate of nearly fifteen miles an hour, a

Trevithick engine carried the first passengers for a short distance in London, on Christmas Eve, 1801. Four years later, a steam engine designed by Trevithick was the first to run on a railway, its tracks laid in Wales. He built a circular track within an enclosure at London, in 1808, and charged admission for a demonstration of a crude steam engine.

Whatever the worth of his accomplishments, Trevithick was more showman than scientist, and his exhibitions were not unlike side shows. His steam-powered vehicles were novelties, not commercial successes.

The high-pressure engine for practical locomotion was made possible by George Stephenson of England (1781–1848). Another onetime miner, he patented, in 1815, a device for attachment of the connecting rod to driving wheels. After that, a locomotive powered by steam compressed in piston boxes was capable of running on rails. In 1825, British rail transportation was effectively under way when a Stephenson engine drew freight and passenger cars on the tracks of the Stockton and Darlington Railway.

The first railroad in the United States was the Baltimore and Ohio, which was opened in 1830 with horse-drawn cars. That same year, a New Yorker, Peter Cooper, demonstrated his successful engine, the *Tom Thumb,* which immediately changed America's railroading to locomotives powered by steam. Steam-powered locomotives moving over rails turned the wheels of progress and opened the way for diesel- and electric-powered trains.

Long experimentation resulted in today's photography:
a technological tool, an art form, an exact method for
visually communicating.

JOSEPH NICÉPHORE NIEPCE
1765–1833, French

LOUIS JACQUES MANDÉ DAGUERRE
1787–1851, French

Two Frenchmen, in one of the most unlikely
collaborations of record, gave impetus to photography in the
early nineteenth century. A young designer of stage sets and
an older man rich enough to indulge in mechanical invention combined their talents, experimenting with photographic process.

The achievement of the two French inventors followed
centuries of attempts by man to make lasting pictorial
records of his own image, his mores, his accomplishments as
warrior, athlete and explorer. Walls of the caves at Lascaux,
France, prove that Cro-Magnon men made drawings
depicting their prowess in the hunt and in battle. Pharaohs
of Egypt, who left the chronicle of their reigns in hiero-
glyphic inscriptions, had their likenesses carved in wood and
stone. Men, savage or primitive, civilized or sophisticated,
made efforts to perpetuate forever their individuality, their

race, their place in history, by the chiseling of statues, miniature or monumental.

It was consistent with man's nature to seek ways to picture people and events for illustration of the printed page after the fifteenth-century development of movable type by Johannes Gutenberg. Although he knew about the *camera obscura,* an instrument for casting an image by the use of a light beam, Gutenberg made no effort to develop it as a means for reproducing pictures. Leonardo da Vinci, the painter and inventor interested in all innovations, suggested in the sixteenth century that the camera obscura might somehow be used as an aid to artists doing portraiture, landscape or still-life pictures.

The camera obscura was a box, dark inside, with a hole through which light rays entered and penetrated a piece of glass, throwing an inverted picture on the solid side of the box opposite to the opening. The very first elementary camera recorded an image without permanently fixing it. The principle of the dark box was described and illustrated in A.D. 989 by an Arabian scholar, Hassan ibn Hassan. There is conclusive evidence that the camera, as he knew it, was a familiar object throughout the Arab world. Roger Bacon, the philosopher-scientist of England, was well informed about the same camera type, which he wrote about in several works, including his *Perspectiva* and *De multiplicatione specierum,* both written in 1267.

In spite of incontrovertible evidence that the light-opening camera principle was known for centuries before the birth of Giambattista della Porta, that Italian architect and sculptor is often credited with the invention of the instrument in 1569. With his camera obscura, meaning "dark room," Porta did show for the first time exactly how artists might make practical use of the device. He constructed little experimental boxes and rigged up an actual room in which a small group of people could be entertained by the camera's images.

The large-scale camera obscura, literally a viewing room, titillated Porta's guests who saw images projected on a wall; light, entering the room through a convex lens, cast "images in action" from outside the room. Ladies and gentlemen on the inside were, in fact, spying on others outside the room; the actions of unsuspecting friends, spouses and officials were beamed by light into the darkened room. Literature of the day abounds in references to the consequences, humorous and dramatic, resulting from the reactions of viewers within the room-sized dark box.

With more serious intent, Porta built a model with a combination of image reflectors previously described by a number of men. He placed a convex lens in an opening at the top of a small box which had a concave mirror tilted at a 45° angle. Light beamed through the opening struck the mirror, which reflected the light downward, and it passed through a second tiny hole, striking a white-surfaced table below. The image there was seen in upright position, not inverted.

Porta demonstrated for the benefit of artists how the outlines of the images, whether of people, scenery or objects, could be traced on the light background receiving surface: paper, cloth or painted board. Artists, penciling or painting the outlined picture, then turned out realistic and salable "artworks" faster and more accurately than others working directly from models: the portrait subject, the landscape or the still-life arrangement. The tracing technique was somewhat analogous to the numbered paintings popular with amateurs of the mid-twentieth century.

Improvement of Porta's invention was made within five years by Daniel Barbaro, who suggested the sharpening of an image by the simple method of moving the surface to be painted either closer to the convex lens-and-light opening, or farther away, as trial and error indicated. He also developed a diaphragm for sharpening images even more, and gave explicit instructions for drawing whatever was beamed from outside through the camera obscura.

For astronomers, the device was an adjunct to telescopic study, and in 1612 a German Jesuit priest attached a telescope to a camera obscura for the purpose of studying sunspots. In about 1600, Johannes Kepler, then mathematician to the Imperial Court of Austria, observed sunspots through the side of a tent in which he had installed a portable camera obscura. The portable model was redesigned by the seventeenth-century British scientist Robert Hooke, who made other improvements of the camera obscura.

Basic research on the camera obscura was a necessary prelude to the development of a permanent fixative for the beamed image. Until then it was ephemeral, disappearing as soon as the light source was cut off, the exceptions being when artists drew or painted the pictured outline.

Scientists, well aware that a chemical treatment of the paper was essential for retaining the image, experimented with numerous fixatives. Breakthroughs came from several men who made no practical use of their research for fixing camera images. Johann Heinrich Schulze found that a solution of silver salt, on bone, wood or paper, turned black when exposed to the sun. His published research was later read by men interested in the phenomenon.

Carl Scheele, a Swedish chemist of the eighteenth century, made his reputation through studies of the action of light on silver chlorides. He proved that light caused silvers to turn black; many previous experimenters claimed that the blackening was due to heat. Scheele also noted the more rapid blackening of silver chlorides by the ultraviolet rays in the spectrum. The conclusion of Scheele about ultraviolet rays was confirmed by the German scientist J. W. Ritter and by Sir William Herschel, the British astronomer who discovered infrared rays.

Deliberate efforts to fix pictures on a material were made by Josiah Wedgwood, British manufacturer of pottery, porcelain and fine china, and by his son Thomas. The father, in 1773, wrote to a friend, "I wish you could send me a good camera obscura, not too cumbersome, that I could take to the gentleman's seat here." He explained that he had a large order from Catherine the Great of Russia, who wanted service china decorated with scenes of famous homes and castles of England. Receiving the requested camera obscura, Josiah Wedgwood, by a time-consuming and far from satisfactory process, projected the "stately homes of England" directly onto individual pieces of china, burning in the designs.

Thomas Wedgwood, after studying the relationships of heat and light at the University of Edinburgh, began to search for some way of "fixing for all times" images on "some type of retaining substance." A long period of cooperative research began for Wedgwood when, in 1797, he met Sir

Humphry Davy, an outstanding chemist and physicist. The two friends experimented with various kinds of chemicals and surface, including paper, white leather and glass. They placed leaves and wings of insects on glass coated with silver nitrate, and then exposed the plate to the sun. The resulting reproduction of the image soon faded for lack of a dependable fixative.

Wedgwood's most successful attempt was with leaves placed on paper soaked in silver nitrate. That part of the paper not covered by leaves turned black when exposed to the sun; the paper under the leaves became pale gray, with the outline and veins of the leaves remaining white. The experiment, while it marked some progress in fixing an image, was far from both Wedgwood's goal and the realization of photographic reproduction.

Photography as it is known today was to be initiated through the efforts of Joseph Nicéphore Niepce, whose father was a King's Counselor to Louis XVI of France. The wealthy family, which had homes at Châlon-sur-Saône and at Gras, lost money and landholdings during the French Revolution, but its aristocratic members were never impoverished.

Nicéphore, born in 1765, was an inventive child who spent his time constructing gadgets in preference to playing children's games. As he grew up, he built working models of machines, some of his own invention. After finishing his military service, Nicéphore and his brother Claude devoted themselves to scientific research and, in 1807, patented an ingeniously designed engine for powering French riverboats.

As in many other instances, chance led to the invention of

modern photography. Claude Niepce, in Paris promoting the engine, sent a camera obscura to Nicéphore in April, 1816. They had wanted pictures of their engine for prospective customers, but had not worked out a satisfactory way to reproduce their design.

Receiving the camera obscura at Gras, Nicéphore set up an attic workroom for experimentation. With the instrument from Paris and with three others purchased from a dealer in Gras, he chose the view from his attic window as the subject for his first picture made on sensitized paper, paper soaked in silver chloride. The scene, recognizable but blurry, faded within a day.

Driven by an urge to find chemicals for permanently fixing the scene, Niepce discarded many solutions over a period of several years during which he beamed the same rural picture into his camera obscuras. He seems never to have become bored by the repetition of the landscape reproduced over and over again, nor to have ever focused on the engine, which he was supposed to picture if possible.

After expensive experimentation, Niepce had the idea of producing a negative film and a positive print of his scene. That original concept of two processes for recording images is the principle on which Niepce's reputation as the inventor of photography is based. With the negative and positive system, he was able to fix many pictures, two still being in existence. But he was unable to fix every picture, the process working only part of the time.

He then tried a more complicated method, covering plates with asphalt varnish which, after long exposure to the sun, became soluble in vegetable oils. Subsequent etching of the plates was followed by development of the prints. The combination of camera image, etching and printing was an advance toward sophisticated photography.

In January, 1826, Niepce ordered several camera obscuras from the Chevaliers, camera-makers in Paris. Chance once more affected the future of photography when Louis Jacques Mandé Daguerre entered the Chevalier shop to order a camera for himself. Fascinated by what he heard about the work of Niepce, Daguerre immediately wrote asking if they might collaborate on research.

Daguerre's father was a clerk to Louis XVI at Orleans. The child, born on November 18, 1787, was brought up on the royal estate where his precocious ability to draw amazed his family, their friends and the courtiers. Apprenticed to an architect at thirteen, the youngster at sixteen studied with I. E. M. Degotti, a noted scenic designer and painter for the Paris Opéra. Quick to learn, Daguerre soon established a reputation that led to commissions of scenery designing for other Parisian theaters.

Daguerre, who had business acumen and a highly developed dramatic sense, was attracted by the potential for profit in the lavish panoramas and dioramas then in vogue. In 1822, he formed the firm of Bouton-Daguerre, with the painter Charles Bouton. They mounted spectacular dioramas, changing pictures excitingly illuminated by imaginative stage-lighting.

The dioramas, accompanied by suitable musical scores, were described as magic by audiences entranced by the displays. To Daguerre and Bouton, there was no magic involved in their *trompe l'oeil* productions. A transparent screen was painted with a colored picture on each side.

Lights skillfully played intermittently on the back and front, creating the effect of a moving picture.

A *Midnight Mass at St. Étienne-du-Mont* was one of Daguerre's most impressive dioramas. On one side of the transparent screen, Bouton painted the empty church of St. Étienne in transparent color; on the reverse side, he painted a congregation in opaque colors. The audience saw first the vast interior of the edifice, lighted with awesome solemnity. That light was slowly dimmed, and a glowing candle illuminated the figure of one person painted on the reverse side of the screen. Slowly candles came on, one at a time, their light, with eerie effectiveness, filling the church with people, and finally showing the priest and acolytes at the altar. For the epic of St. Étienne, Daguerre and Bouton chose a screen sixty-nine feet wide and forty-five feet high, which was placed thirty-two feet from the first row of the audience.

For a command performance ordered by Louis Philippe, the two designers outdid all earlier productions. They presented sylvan landscapes with chalets, stands of trees, fields of flowers, peasants, and shepherds with flocks; the scenes, changed by subtle lighting, were accompanied by the ringing of cowbells, by the singing of mountain ballads.

The partners, hailed on the Continent for their artistic endeavors, opened a diorama in Regents Park, London, in 1823. An immediate success, the London venture, for which a special building had to be erected, added considerable profits to the Bouton-Daguerre company.

While designing dioramas, Daguerre read everything published about attempts to fix images for a long period, if not permanently. He envisioned that accomplishment as another method for producing dramatic presentations. Although ever a showman, Daguerre cannot be denigrated because of his original purpose in delving into the art and science of photography.

To conduct his own research with fixed images, he established a laboratory where a small staff helped him with secret experiments on which he worked for long hours. His concentration created a domestic crisis. His wife, a down-to-earth Englishwoman, resenting his lack of attention to her, suggested that he might be losing his mind. Madame Daguerre's nagging stopped after she discreetly consulted with chemists and others knowledgeable about fixed-image procedures. Reassured by what she learned, she optimistically awaited greater family fame and fortune than that realized through the dioramas.

Daguerre seriously wanted to make a valuable contribution to mankind and foresaw the far-reaching impact of the camera and the photographs taken with it. In that mood of anticipation and high hopes, he entered the shop of the Chevaliers on the very day when talk there centered on the experiments of Nicéphore Niepce.

Niepce, receiving the letter from Daguerre suggesting joint research, was uninterested. He was sixty-one years old, moody, discouraged by repeated failures, yet confident that, by himself, he could perfect his photographic processes.

He did, however, enter into correspondence with Daguerre. They continued their independent research, sending each other samples of their photographs but neither revealing any information about the processes. At last, after sixteen months, Niepce, his resources drained by the experiments, agreed to meet Daguerre. They signed a ten-year agreement, each to receive a half-share of any profits.

Niepce's contribution to the partnership was a certain, if inconsistent, success with scientific methods for capturing images and fixing them to materials; Daguerre's, a sophisticated knowledge of cameras and of lighting, and indisputable promotional ability.

The word *photograph* was not yet known to Niepce and Daguerre who referred to their pictures as drawings from light, fixed images and living lithographs. The word *photography* appeared in an article written by a German astronomer and published on February 25, 1839. On February 2 of that year, Sir Charles Wheatstone had used the word in a letter to William Henry Fox Talbot, both men being vitally interested in the permanent fixing of images. Throughout 1839, members of the Royal Society heard papers in which the words *photograph* and *photography* were used and described. The word *photograph* stems from the ancient Greek: Φῶς, Φῶτος = light, and Γράψω, Γράψως = write.

The partnership of Daguerre and Niepce was destined to be considerably shorter than the term of agreement because, at the end of four years, the latter died. During his work with Daguerre, Niepce made pictures on glass and developed copper plates. He described the glass experiments as having results which, "though imperfect, appear deserving of notice, because this species of application may be brought more easily to perfection and become in the sequel a most interesting department of heliography," meaning the use of the sun as the light source. The copper plates with which Niepce experimented were covered with silver and then exposed to vapor of iodine, a method that did strengthen the image.

By contract with Daguerre, Niepce's son Isidore inherited his father's interest in the business. Isidore, scientifically informed, had long worked with his father. Together they produced and sold lithographs in demand throughout Europe; unable to obtain lithographic limestone locally, they substituted pewter plates for their pictures. Isidore, competent to carry forward his father's work with copper plates, stayed on with Daguerre.

In October, 1837, chance again was responsible for progress in the development of photography. Daguerre stored, in a chemical cupboard, several plates he thought were ruined. A few days later, preparing to wash the damaged plates for reuse, he removed them from the cupboard. To his astonishment images on the plates were sharply fixed, the pictures as clear as if he were looking at a natural scene. He hastily took everything from the shelves, trying to find out what might have happened. Unable to discover an explanation, Daguerre coated a number of plates, each with a different chemical, and shut all in the closet. Again every stored plate had a clear and fixed image. Perplexed, Daguerre once more emptied the shelves, examining every article. That second time, he noticed a few glistening globules which had leaked out of a cracked bottle of mercury.

Thinking that mercury might be the chemical agent that developed and sharpened the pictures, Daguerre at once held a prepared plate over a container of heated mercury, and its rising vapor produced a clear image. Working all night, he ran repeated tests and, by dawn, knew that no more than a twenty-minute exposure was necessary for mercury vapor to produce a perfect picture.

Daguerre's camera was made of two boxes. The one at the back had a ground-glass slide separating it from the front and larger box, which contained the lenses. The back box could be slipped into the front box for the purpose of extending the focal length. When closed, the boxes measured ten inches; when pulled apart for picture-taking, twenty inches. The plates were six and one-half inches by eight and one-half inches. Exposure time, originally twenty minutes, was reduced to three minutes. The camera's opening, which admitted the light for proper exposure, could be enlarged or made smaller. It was crude but added quality of reproduction to the daguerreotypes. This is now known as F-stops of the diaphragm.

At first Daguerre claimed that mercury vapor consistently fixed a photograph, but experience proved it did not. Two more years of experimentation were to pass before Daguerre developed a completely reliable fixative, a solution of salt and hot water. The standard and reliable daguerreotype was at last a reality.

In an attempt to assure for himself the historic honor of being the inventor of the photographic process, Daguerre tried to dissolve the partnership with Isidore Niepce, who firmly refused. Earlier, Niepce had signed an agreement that the company should be known only by Daguerre's name. On the second occasion, Niepce once more conceded that Daguerre should have public credit, but insisted on retaining his rights to one half of the financial returns until the termination of the ten-year contract made with Nicéphore Niepce.

The people-oriented Daguerre used his camera primarily for portraiture, but his first daguerreotype was a floral still life which he gave to Monsieur de Cailleix, a curator of the Louvre. That picture is now owned and often displayed by *la Société Française de Photographie* in Paris.

Daguerreotypes won international fame for Daguerre. The day after he patented his process in London, he gave his French patent to the government in return for a generous life pension. Rich beyond the expectations of his practical wife, Daguerre bought a villa at Bry; there, from 1840 on, he regally held court, receiving distinguished visitors, French and foreign. To amuse himself, he painted a scene behind the altar of the local church. Another *trompe l'oeil,* his painting in perspective makes the small church seem to be twice its length.

The limitlessly imaginative Daguerre died at Bry in 1851, leaving as his major legacy the photographs on metal that bear his name, the family heirlooms treasured by descendants of the famous and the obscure, the worldly and the shy, who were daguerreotyped for posterity.

AND AFTER

The camera excited the imagination of experimenters everywhere. In France, Claude Felix Abel Niepce de Saint-Victor, with chemical albumins, produced steel-engraving photographs. England's William Henry Fox Talbot, at thirty-four, while sketching at Lake Como in Italy, decided that the camera obscura was better suited to faithful reproduction than a pencil in his unskilled hand. That conclusion led to a milestone in the history of photography: Talbot's negative-postive method for producing photographs on paper.

Long a stationary instrument, unwieldy and heavy, the camera was made in portable sizes. Miniature cameras weighing "only eight pounds" were sold to an eager public.

The first photographic portrait in the United States was made by John William Draper, who improved the quality of daguerreotypes. Another American who experimented with daguerreotypes was the artist-inventor Samuel F. B. Morse, famous for the first telegraphic message, "What hath God wrought," sent by Morse code.

The search for practical and inexpensive photographic film ended in the United States with the founding of the Eastman Kodak Company at Rochester, New York. George Eastman, more businessman than experimenter, introduced the stripping film of paper in 1888. There followed his firm's roll film to be inserted into a camera, a film that reduced camera operations to three steps, a lighter weight camera, and a system for taking one hundred photographs without reloading the camera.

Eastman coined the commercial slogan, "You press the button, we do the rest." Photographers, professional and amateur, sent their cameras to Rochester where the company developed and printed the film and then, by mail, shipped the camera, negatives and prints to the customer. Eastman, controlling the manufacture and sale of the only American roll-film camera, built a multimillion-dollar business, and made Kodak a household word.

As early as July, 1839, Sir William Herschel experimented with color photographs, capturing the spectrum on film. His photographs were not fixed, but Sir William pointed the way for others. The basic principle of color photography was established in 1861 by James Clerk Maxwell, the Scottish physicist. He developed the theory of color separation, the blue, green and red emulsion of film. The emulsions captured on photographic film the reds, blues and greens of light reflected from objects, and provided the negative basis from which color prints were made.

Maxwell's basic idea was developed to the practical stage by L. D. Mannes and L. Godowsky of the Eastman Kodak Company. Perfected in 1935, the Mannes-Godowsky process made color photography available to all.

Cameras now are the "new eyes of science," being used in research laboratories of universities and industry, in space and underwater explorations, and in crime investigation. The portable camera is light enough to be slung from a shoulder strap; the miniature camera is weighed by the ounce, not the pound. The black light of invisible rays, ultraviolet and infrared, and the bright light of the sun's rays are sources used by men with cameras.

In a little more than a century, the camera has emerged from the obscurity of workshops where individuals experimented with techniques of picture-processing and the construction of instruments for picture-taking. Modern photography is a hobby, an art form, an invaluable tool of technology. And it annually produces $25 billion in business in the United States alone.

Mechanical calculations for science and industry were a nineteenth-century dream realized by the twentieth-century computer.

CHARLES BABBAGE
1792–1871, British

Notable mathematicians abounded in England during the early nineteenth century, and high in their ranks was Charles Babbage, a man born one hundred years too soon. His thinking was typical twentieth century; his projection was to automation. Babbage did time-and-motion studies for industry, made contributions to what is now called operations research, and forecast today's digital computers with his own calculating machines. Those inventions involved him in controversy for most of his adult life which was stormy in all its public aspects.

The calculating machine for speeding arithmetical computations was the invention of Blaise Pascal (1623–1662) who, while still a teen-ager, began the design of a computing machine to help his mathematician father with calculations. Geared wheels used in such a device for the first time made possible additions and subtractions. Pascal's machine, which looked like a face-tissue box, had eight rotatable wheels, each with zero to nine on its circumference. Dials on top of the oblong casing showed values of hundreds of thousands from left to right for six spaces; the last two spaces at the far right were for decimals.

An improved calculating machine made by Baron Gottfried von Leibniz (1646–1716) had a stepped-drum, or stepped-wheel, mechanism and featured a cylinder in graduation proportionate to the numerals one through nine. The machine, operated by a cogwheel, added each number to the one before it. The first commercial mechanical calculator, 1820, was based on the Leibniz principle; built by the French inventor Charles Xavier Thomas, the machine added, subtracted, multiplied, divided, and extracted roots.

A register, composed of a set of wheels with ten positions around each circumference, like that of Leibniz, is basic to the mechanical calculating machine. The register, properly positioned with the wheel corresponding to the written number, becomes a counter by use of a carry from one wheel to the next. A complete arithmetical operation results from the cycle of action, each action instituting the next. The result is shown on a counter, the accumulator; it has an addition feed when the wheels move simultaneously by amounts that correspond to the number being added.

Leibniz designed a means for storing the carry during the addition feed, and then adding the carries, one by one, in a carry wave. Babbage developed a variation for shortening the time of the carry wave, especially in an electrically operated machine. But Babbage was not interested in simple calculating machines of the type commonly used for limited office procedures and in stores. He was concerned with using mathematical theories for facilitating complex research in various scientific fields.

Born in Devonshire, the day after Christmas in 1792, Charles Babbage had a banker-father and a mother who understood her son's preoccupation with invention. Even in her old age, Mrs. Babbage actively encouraged the middle-aged Charles to continue with the design of his analytical engine, in spite of criticism, widespread and disheartening.

Charles was prepared for Cambridge by tutors, after attending an academy where he was introduced to algebra by *Ward's Young Mathematician's Guide.* Intrigued by numbers and by problems of arithmetic, Charles habitually arose at three in the morning and, for a couple of predawn hours, studied mathematics in the privacy of a chilly classroom.

At Cambridge, Babbage made lasting friendships with several bon vivants, his comrades in sailing, opponents at chess, and partners in pranks and at card-playing. When he found a lack of tutorial enthusiasm for the mathematics which fascinated him, he drew up plans for the Analytical Society, whose members, to a man, became distinguished. The university's dons disapproved of the Society, which nonetheless flourished, even sponsoring the publication of *Transactions,* a volume by Babbage and John Herschel, afterward by Sir J. F. W. Herschel, lifelong staunch and devoted supporter of Babbage.

The Analytical Society held its meetings in a rented room where members seriously discussed and vehemently argued about the mathematical theories of Sir Isaac Newton, Leibniz and S. F. Lacroix. Babbage pondered the theory of functional equations of all orders, memorized the master work on differential and integral calculus written by Lacroix, and partially translated a calculus treatise by the same French mathematician.

In 1814, the year that Babbage took his Cambridge degree, he married and moved into the London home of his father; Benjamin Babbage graciously supported his son, who set up a workshop in the family's carriage house. There he was free for self-centered concentration on theoretical projects and inventive experiments. Never a conventional family man, Babbage was convivial with scientific friends, keeping up a lively correspondence with several in England and on the Continent. In Paris with Herschel, the newly married Babbage met the outstanding mathematicians of France, becoming friends with several.

Babbage was a founding member of the Royal Astronomical Society, and at its first meeting in February, 1820, Herschel gave the opening address. Shortly after, Babbage and Herschel, by appointment, were engaged in producing calculations of astronomical tables for the Society. The two collaborators decided on formulas that were to be reduced into numbers by calculators—these were men, not machines. The calculator, a specialist at numbers, was retained to do routine but time-consuming arithmetical computations. The profession of the calculators was outmoded in time by some of the very inventions for which their services were originally required.

There were many errors in the columns of numbers submitted by calculators to Herschel and Babbage, and the latter expressed the wish that the calculations had been done by "steam," that is, mechanically. Several years earlier, at the Analytical Society room in Cambridge, he had remarked that a table of logarithms with which he was working could probably be calculated by a machine. In correspondence he frequently mentioned arduous research into functions, the relationship of mathematical magnitudes, the numbers arbitrarily given to quantities by set rules. The idea of mechanical computations and the need for them in research obviously were long in Babbage's mind.

Babbage's first little model for calculations was a machine for computation of tables by differences, a difference being the amount by which one magnitude differs from another of the same kind, in greater or less amounts. The model had three figure-wheels on the table axis: one wheel on the second difference, two on the first. Some parts were made in Babbage's own carriage workshop; other parts, under contract at machine shops. Assembling was done by Babbage, and after he corrected faulty framework and supports, he successfully tested the model by calculating several very elementary tables.

He read a paper on his difference engine to the Royal Astronomical Society in June, 1822, and elaborated on his plans in a July letter to Sir Humphry Davy, president of the Royal Society. In the letter Babbage, a member of the Society, went beyond the machine for calculating any required table but limited to two orders of differences. He explained that his first machine could readily be converted to extract roots of equations and roots of numbers. Other machines on his drawing board were so complex that only a few theoretical mathematicians could understand their principles, and only inventors, the enormity of the construction job in terms of time and money required.

Babbage's difference engine was designed for labor-saving in three areas: one, analytical for determining formulas; two, analytical and arithmetical; and three, tabulation, the results to be taken down by a staff of number copiers. Perfection of a printing mechanism for receiving the calculated pages in type would, according to the inventor, further reduce the number of people employed for "reading" the difference engine.

The Chancellor of the Exchequer of the government, in July, 1823, informed the Royal Society that Babbage had been awarded £1,500 toward construction of the difference engine. At that time the inventor expected the completion of the machine within three years and the total cost to be no more than £5,000, he to pay whatever the amount above the government advance. Babbage was plagued for the rest of his life by misunderstanding about the original government transaction, and for lack of written record, the controversy over the terms was never resolved.

Construction of the difference engine was begun under the supervision of Babbage, who was without experience in either mechanics or engineering. An outstanding toolmaker, Joseph Clement, retained by Babbage, directed teams of men who made the tools that later they were to use in the construction of sections of the engine. The inventor himself worked out a mechanical notation system for tracing the motion of every piece of the machinery from start to finish. He determined what framework was adequate for the support of various sections and that those were of necessary strength and of essential maneuverability. The interdependence of the parts presented monumental problems, and Babbage discarded many more drawings of the interacting operations than he ever used.

Little progress had been made on the engine, in spite of consistent and often frenzied application to it by Babbage, when in 1827 he collapsed from sorrow. He lost, within months of each other, his understanding father, his adored wife, and two children. Some years later his own daughter died in her teens, and only three of Babbage's seven sons grew to adulthood.

In addition to his personal grief of 1827, Babbage suffered a professional blow when Professor George Biddell Airy, later Sir George Airy, called the difference engine a "humbug," influencing by his statement the uninformed opinion of several others quick to accuse Charles Babbage of wasting the government's cash advance.

Too ill to continue with his invention, Babbage went to Europe for an extended stay. He was feted everyplace and much honored in Italy, where he learned of his appointment as Lucasian Professor of Mathematics, the Chair of Newton, at Cambridge. Briefly Babbage thought of declining the post because he had earlier been bitterly disappointed by having the coveted professorship go to Airy, Babbage and one other being passed over. On second thought Babbage, from Rome, accepted the Chair of Newton and held the professorship for ten years without giving a single lecture.

Returning to England late in 1828, Babbage was immediately caught up in altercations about the construction of the machine. In his absence, Herschel had supervised the work carried forward by Clement, with whom Babbage had been in constant communication by mail, answering questions posed by the toolmaker and inspecting his drawings of suggested designs of parts.

By approval of His Grace the Duke of Wellington, then Prime Minister of England, Babbage, in 1829, received a second grant of £1,500, followed soon after by a grant of an additional £3,000. There followed an exchange of complicated correspondence about who would own the machine and for what parts of construction Babbage and the government would respectively be responsible. Early in 1830, the government put up more money, stating that the machine was to be their property and that Babbage, at the completion, would be reimbursed for any private expenditures approved by inspecting engineers.

The arrangement with the government was complicated by Clement, who, from 1824 through 1830, accumulated exorbitant expenses, mostly labor costs. The toolmaker, personally on salary to Babbage, presented a statement of expenses of more than £7,000 in December, 1830. After consideration of the bill and at the suggestion of Babbage, the government arranged to remove machine parts from Clement's workshop. When fireproof accommodations were eventually constructed near Babbage's home, Clement refused to cooperate in any way. Dismissing the project's workmen, Clement attached designs for the machine and kept all tools, including many specifically made by Babbage.

For four or five years after work on the difference engine was halted in 1834 by Clement, Babbage consulted with the government about his designs and detailed plans for an analytical engine, a machine with greater simplicity than the difference engine and with infinitely greater capability. By use of punched cards like those of the Jacquard loom of 1801, the analytical engine was to simplify by thousands of parts instead of the 120 similar parts of Babbage's first engine, still not completed.

In his own country Babbage found a lack of understanding about what he proposed and about the relationship of his two machines, the partially completed difference engine and the analytical, designed to encompass all of a science's calculations. With complications typical of a bureaucracy, the government delayed decisions about construction of the analytical engine and quibbled about continuing with the difference engine, which might be obsolete before completion.

Beset in England, a troubled Babbage again found Italy a haven when, in 1841, he returned there for a meeting of scientists, some already excited by advance reports about the new machine. L. F. Menabrea, an outstanding mathematician, later the Prime Minister of Italy, which he helped to unify, was appreciative of Babbage's machine and published the first paper on it in 1842.

By the time of publication of Menabrea's paper, which was written in French, Babbage was back in England and again embroiled with the government in the person of Sir Robert Peel, the Prime Minister. The government decided to turn over to Babbage all parts and designs of the difference engine, as it then existed, and so informed the inventor on November 4, 1842. It was all but twenty years since Babbage, in an interview never accurately recorded, had understood that the difference engine was to be built for the government and with government funds. It was just under nine years since the construction of the first part of the machine.

With various parts incomplete and no prospect of the whole being assembled, the government gave up any claim to the difference engine, assigning to Babbage ninety boxes filled with indexed and numbered plans, and a finished portion of the machine that Babbage refused to keep. The difference engine was completely designed and its principles detailed on plans, and Babbage turned his full attention to the analytical engine, which he prophetically considered to be of historical significance in the future of science.

The analytical engine, when properly set up, or as we know it today, programmed, could follow the equivalent of thought processes. It could not think, but its brain, holding symbols of wide variety and amounts, was made to function practically and theoretically. In operation, the engine mechanically substituted for the mental work of the human being and executed calculations with speed and precision. Like many inventions, this one of Babbage's was an object of ridicule, but its successful completion was not prevented by public scorn and derision. The inventor himself was guilty of procrastination and, in part, was to blame for altercations which delayed production.

Menabrea's paper on the analytical engine was translated and fully annotated by the incredible Lady Lovelace, only legitimate daughter of Lord Byron. Then just twenty-seven, she was called genius by many male contemporaries who marveled at her ability to reason and to think through complicated mathematical and metaphysical problems. Lady Lovelace and Babbage wrote back and forth in great detail about her notes, which expanded Menabrea's paper by two thirds.

When her translation was published in the late summer of 1843, the Italian mathematician, by then General Menabrea, was much pleased with the accurate presentation, although some interpretations varied from his own. Lady Lovelace foresaw that an analytical engine might, in some cases, make a choice of action; Menabrea thought of the machine as an automation without possible variations after it was activated. The Italian analyst had done a masterful job of explaining Babbage's second engine, a machine representing numbers dependent on operation cards and variable cards. A third kind of card was for numbers of Bernoulli and others; the cards, in combination, could be inserted into the machine to avoid repetitious computation. Lady Lovelace, no less than the original author, grasped the concept and principle of Babbage's machine and made indisputable contributions of clarification for scholars who read her work in English.

Babbage completed detailed plans for the analytical engine by 1848, but only certain portions were ever built. For nearly twenty years he assured people that the analytical engine would be finished, although he must have known the falsity of his statement. He continued to bicker with the government, to be entrapped by bitter adversaries, and to be diverted by interests and projects in no way allied to his phenomenal calculating machines that were so many decades in advance of their time.

An incredibly energetic man, Babbage nonetheless tended to spread himself thin. When he was at first working on the difference engine model, he took time out to worry about postal rates, rigging a model for delivery of mail encased in small cylinders released to travel on overhead wires. After a descent in a diving bell, he wrote an encyclopedia article suggesting a future reality: the blockade-running submarine. During his European trip of 1827, he fitted a calash into the counterpart of a modern trailer. There was a bunk for him to sleep on in comfort; closets for suits, dinner clothes and greatcoats to hang full length; drawers for his small clothes; compartments for storage of plans and sketches of his inventions; and even a heating unit for beverages and for cooking breakfast and any other light meal.

Babbage turned down both a baronetcy and a knighthood, vigorously expressing himself in favor of life peerages, because so many hereditary peers were, to understate his expressed opinion, quite unworthy. He was a founding member and first chairman of the Statistical Society of London; he dabbled in religion and wrote a ballet for which he invented colored stage lighting. With Lord and Lady Lovelace, he attempted to work out an infallible betting system for racing; there were unfortunate consequences for Lady Lovelace, an inveterate and unlucky gambler, who was possessive about the "book," or betting guide, on which the three partners labored for a long time.

As early as 1831, Babbage published his twenty-one volumes of *Specimens of Logarithmic Tables,* and toward the end of his life wrote *Passage from the Life of a Philosopher,* a strange autobiography because of its gaps and lapses, but a book with a style as lively and attention-holding as a twentieth-century best seller. His 1832 book *On the Economy of Machinery and Manufactures* is a primer of present-day operational research. He thought that industrial problems could be solved by scientific methods—and made notes for a book, commonly called *Economy of Manufactures*—in individual workshops and at large factories.

In banking, Babbage was retained as an efficiency expert to advise on printing and engraving and, in 1836, to inspect counterfeit banknotes, devising, if possible, ways to detect and prevent forgery. As adviser to the directors of the Great Western Railway, Babbage made practical experiments with a car which he personally outfitted. He spent five months and several hundred pounds on the railroading problem, eventually suggesting certain essentials for safe and efficient operation: every engine to have a mechanical self-registering device for recording velocity through the operation; a dynamometer, or strong spring, for measuring the force exerted by the engine, to be placed between it and the first car of the train; a means of recording, for reference in case of accident, the curve made by the center of the engine on the plane of the tracks.

The disparity of Babbage's activities was incredible. He long protested against the presence in the streets of organ grinders and other strolling musicians who disturbed his train of thought by the strains of their incessant music. For children he designed a mechanical toy, a tick-tack-toe game that was never constructed, although he once thought of raising funds through exhibition of the device with automation players. His ophthalmoscope, the instrument for examining the inner eye, was the subject of a paper published in 1854.

Friction developed over his model of occulting lights for lighthouses and night-signaling because top prizes of the exhibition, where he hoped to show it, were given out before the completion of his entry. Frequent rejections of his inventions by officials of exhibitions in England distressed Babbage, who became more bitter at each exclusion. His occulting solar-light model was shown in 1853 at Brussels, where Babbage generously permitted a Russian to borrow the only existing paper on the invention. Oddly enough, Babbage seems not to have been irate when he learned that an identical light system was used by Russians at the 1854–1856 seige of Sebastopol.

The unpredictable Babbage not only was gracious about a Swedish difference engine inspired by an article about his own, but promoted the cause of the inventor at the Great International Exhibition at Paris, in 1855. The Swedish printer, M. Scheutz, who made the small engine which was less complicated than Babbage's, was awarded the French Gold Medal for his workable model that proved what Babbage never doubted: The difference engine was practical.

AND AFTER

The mathematical engines invented by Charles Babbage were, in principle, on the order of today's computers. These have ever increasing capabilities so great that it is easy to lose sight of the impact that adding machines and other mechanical calculators had on business, industry and research.

Frank S. Baldwin (1838–1925), inventor of a recording lumber-measure, also built a calculating machine that added, subtracted, multiplied and divided. In his St. Louis, Missouri, workshop, Baldwin employed a clever model-maker, William S. Burroughs, who later in his own right became an inventor and manufacturer of office machinery. With William J. Monroe, Baldwin redesigned his first engine, producing a cylinder type with nine numbered retractable teeth, or pins, and a cover plate with nine numbers in slots. A slot number was set to correspond with a cylinder number, and the machine's operation was activated by either a lever or a keyboard. Baldwin patented a calculating machine in 1890 and a calculator in 1902.

Burroughs, who gained experience by making models of castings and various inventions, began work on his adding machine in 1880. He took out a first patent in 1885, and patented a key-set adding machine with crank in 1888.

The office machines of the late nineteenth century and early twentieth shortened procedures of bookkeeping in corner grocery stores and in huge factories; in retail and wholesale businesses; in centers of manufacture, transportation and government. The inventions unquestionably contributed to the efficiency and accuracy of mathematical calculations in many areas of endeavor, but failed to have the scope of the complicated engines designed by Babbage.

In 1930, Dr. Vannevar Bush completed a diffierential analyzer which, mechanically operated, was capable of solving differential equations. A little more than a decade later it was constructed for both electrical and mechanical operation. A properly named *Complex Computer,* built on the principle of the telephone switchboard, was a 1940 pioneering machine in the field of automation.

There are two kinds of computers: the analog and the digital. The former is a highly sophisticated machine which, by electric voltages and shaft rotations, solves mathematical problems without registering the results in numbers. The digital computer completes its multiple operations by numbers, and in most cases results are automatically printed at the completion of the operation. There is an input of data suitable for the particular computer, an output for results, a storage unit for recording procedural steps, an arithmetic unit with operational circuits, and a programming unit which is the operational control.

Whether electronic or mechanical, which is less common today, the computer is capable of doing complex mathematics at high speed. Not so long ago, it was directly programmed by an individual; increasingly today it is programmed through machines operated either electrically or electronically.

Computers smaller than the proverbial breadbox speed up office procedures; computers of square-block dimensions can operate an automated factory. With a read-out of statistics, projections and analysis, the computer is invaluable to the research scientist. The computer lessens election-night tension because returns are electronically forecast within minutes after the closing of the last polling place.

In three centuries the calculating machine has progressed from a simple manual device to an electronic wonder, benefiting millions yet comprehended by relatively few. Like its elementary predecessors, the computer is unable to think but, as programmed by man, it can approximate his mental processes.

The sewing machine made possible mass production in factories and aided the seamstress at home and in industry.

ELIAS HOWE
1819–1867, American

Few men have as many misfortunes throughout life as Elias Howe, and few as much good luck as he ultimately enjoyed. His frail body, which almost miraculously survived the rigors of frugal living and the tensions of business problems, lasted long enough for him to amass a fortune through a court ruling upholding his patent rights to the first practical sewing machine.

Elias Howe, Jr., was the son of an industrious but poor New England farmer who, to support a wife and eight children, supplemented his income by milling grist and lumber. When Elias was only six, he, along with other children in the family, earned much-needed pennies by piecework, hand-sewing wire teeth into cards for local cotton mills.

Industriousness and inventiveness ran in the Howe family. Two uncles share with Elias the commemorative honors on the Howe monument at Spencer, the Massachusetts village where he was born in 1819. His Uncle William engineered a truss for support of bridges and roofs; Uncle Tyler designed a spring bed and numerous gadgets and appliances for household use.

The mill machinery on the Howe farm fascinated young Elias, who watched them roll and grind, plane and split, increasing production and lessening hand labor. Although he helped with light chores in the barnyard, Elias, because of his dexterity with tools, was more often the family's repairman. As upkeep of his parents' house required, he was glazier, solderer and carpenter; a willing and expert handyman, Elias asked for no help and efficiently completed every job undertaken. Tenacity exhibited when he was a child became a characteristic for which he was noted as an adult.

For lack of funds to clothe and feed him, Elias, at twelve, left school and home to become a hired hand for a neighboring farmer. The youngster, handicapped by a slight limp and general poor health, was unsuited for heavy farm labor day after day, from dawn to dusk. Within the year he returned home and, until he was sixteen, ran and repaired his father's mill machinery, gaining experience that was later was to be invaluable.

In 1835, Howe again left home and, at Lowell, Massachusetts, worked for a manufacturer of cotton machinery until the panic of 1837 forced the shutdown of mills. In a Cambridge machine shop, Howe was foreman of hemp-carding, dull work that paid little. Moving in to Boston, he obtained employment with Ari Davis, a maker of watches and surveying instruments, who was often commissioned by Harvard professors to design special apparatus for scientific research projects. Howe benefited from association with the creative Davis and from the mechanical challenges presented by customers of the shop.

A chance remark made by Davis, in 1839, was the inspiration for Howe's ambition to build a sewing machine. Howe overheard a conversation between a local inventor and Davis, who idly boasted that he himself could make a sewing machine. The inventor answered that, if that were true, Davis could become rich. Howe decided on the spot to make a machine that would solve his financial problems. Then married and the father of two, he was barely able to exist on his salary from Davis: nine dollars a week.

For the next four years, Howe mulled over the design of a sewing machine and the technical difficulties of producing one. Small chain-stitch machines were already in use and sewing-machine designs existed, but Howe knew nothing about either the American or European models. These, obscure and not in production, had certain component designs that would have been useful, sparing him from lengthy trial-and-error experimentation.

His first attempt at uniform stitching was unsuccessful because he copied the movement of a needle in handsewing. The result was irregularity of stitching. Discarding that technique, he began work on a design quite different in principle. He replaced a needle, which had an eye in the middle, with the eye-pointed needle previously used by generations of thatchers and lacemakers. At about the same time that Howe chose the eye-pointed needle, it was incorporated into a chain-stitch machine of British patent and in a sewing machine designed by Walter Hunt of New York.

The sewing machine that Howe worked out, detail by detail in his head, not on a drawing board, was for lock-stitching. Hunt's was the same type but, being faulty in performance, was neither put into production nor patented. Hunt, probably discouraged, turned his attention to numerous lesser inventions, including a safety pin and a paper collar, with fool-the-eye simulated stitching.

The lock stitch, favored by Howe and Hunt, was formed by a shuttle like those in many kinds of looms well known to both men. Under the cloth being sewn, the threaded needle made a loop through which the shuttle was thrown to interweave the two threads, making the lock stitch. The line of stitching was even when the motion of needle and shuttle was regular and uniform.

It is an oversimplification to state that Howe's first model, when tested, produced a straight and satisfactory seam. Elias Howe needed his fortitude and optimism to bear the vicissitudes of the construction period. In order to concentrate on his invention, he left Ari Davis and went to live with Elias Howe, Sr., then residing in Cambridge. In theory Elias, Jr., was to support himself and his family with odd jobs, but in practice he did little but work on the sewing machine. When his father suffered financial loss from a fire, the younger Howe was in desperate straits, not for the last time.

His personal and financial affairs were temporarily resolved in 1844 by a friend, George Fisher, who took the Howe family into his home as guests. Fisher's faith in Elias was confirmed by a loan of $500 for materials to complete the machine model; in return, Fisher was to have one-half share in the invention.

The sewing machine, completed in the spring of 1845, was an unwieldy-looking table model. It was powered by a hand-operated flywheel attached to an overhanging arm. The top thread on a large spool, or bobbin, at the lower left of the machine, was fed to the curved eye-pointed needle set on another arm. The cloth was vertically suspended on pins; the vibrating needle arm and a baster- or feeder-plate were co-ordinated to move the cloth forward evenly after each stitch was locked. Under the cloth a rod-driven shuttle, wound with thread, vibrated back and forth to complete the lock stitch.

Howe's machine, incorporating basic principles of today's latest models, had one major limitation: it produced only straight stitching. There was need for a better means of feeding material by a wheel system that permitted sewing in any direction. Sewing machines were soon equipped with variations of that feature. John J. Greenough invented a wheel-feed for sewing straight, curved or angled seams, and for the same purpose Allen B. Wilson designed first a two-motion feed and then a four-motion feed.

Howe, after making several minor adjustments, primarily for relieving tension that pulled stitches, demonstrated his sewing machine in April, 1845. He personally operated the machine at a local clothing manufacturer's plant, competing with five of the factory's speediest seamstresses. He sewed 250 stitches a minute, seven times the number possible by hand; and his seams were smoother, straighter and, in every way, better than those of any of the women who sewed by hand.

Tailors attending Howe's demonstration reacted to the machine as a novelty of no economic interest. Even manufacturers, who recognized its worth as a machine for making straight-seam products like sheets, quilts and skirts, were resistant to it on two counts: price and labor. At $300 apiece, the dozens of machines needed for a factory's conversion to mechanical operation represented a substantial investment. What's more, employers reasonably concluded that workers, irked by the necessity to take training in machine operation, might also be fearful of layoffs resulting from a process already demonstrated as more efficient than manual methods.

While manufacturers in Massachusetts arrived independently at their reluctance to risk labor-management conflict, there was a prior instance of such a crisis in France. It was sparked by the workable sewing machine invented in 1830 by Barthelemi Thimonnier. His machine, with a pressure-foot feed system and a crochet needle, was capable of 200 chain stitches a minute. In 1841, French army uniforms were turned out by operators of eighty of Thimonnier's sewing machines. Tailors and seamstresses, recognizing the stitching machine as an invention that jeopardized their livelihood, mobbed Thimonnier's workshop and systematically destroyed every machine.

Recovering from the loss by 1848, he then built a few more machines; but they did not sell in France, and his designs were not carried forward. Years after, the presser-foot feed was introduced as an original design by an inventor who had never heard of Thimonnier's machine.

Only Howe's perseverance kept his machine from being stored as a curio in some loft or machine shop, the design shelved like Thimonnier's. Howe took his second model to Washington to be patented, after a delay caused by lack of cash. His friend Fisher once again advanced the money, paying the patent fee and round-trip travel expenses for both of them to Washington. In the nation's capital, Howe demonstrated his sewing machine at a local fair, attracting large crowds and excited comments, but no buyers.

Fisher was disheartened by the experience, but Howe was yet hopeful that his machine would be a financial success.

He was convinced of its commercial value, although he, at the time, was $2,000 in debt and living again in his father's house.

Elias, Jr., personally penniless, managed to raise money to send his brother Amasa Howe, by steerage, to England where manufacturing was done on a wider scale than in the United States. There would have been no interest in an American sewing machine had the British known about a similar invention by one of their own countrymen, Thomas Saint. In 1790, he patented a chain-stitch sewing machine with a sturdy overhang arm and a horizontal cloth-plate, features later to be standard in sewing machines. Even Saint might have improved his machine by a double-pointed needle designed in 1755 by Charles F. Weisenthal, a British inventor. The double-pointed needle, another standard component of future sewing machines, was long overlooked by subsequent designers.

Saint's model, with its efficient features, was disregarded in his own day; the scale drawing, filed at the Patent Office, was not examined by any other sewing-machine designer until 1850. The important components of Saint's machine, like those of Thimonnier's, were redesigned by later inventors as originals.

Unaware of the existence of the patent for a sewing machine in his own country, William Thomas, of London, bought Elias Howe's second model for $1,217. As it turned out, the deal was not a fortunate one for Howe. Thomas, who manufactured umbrellas, corsets and shoes, was given the patent rights for England, in return for a royalty to Howe of $14.60 on every machine. For years Thomas collected royalties of about fifty dollars a machine from British manufacturers, but never paid one cent of royalty to Elias Howe, who had Thomas' word but not a written royalty agreement.

Amasa Howe returned to Cambridge with the purchase money for his brother and an offer to Elias from Thomas, who needed a specific sewing machine for mass production of corsets. The inventor and Amasa went to London where they were set up in a well-equipped workshop by Thomas. He soon after advanced money to Elias Howe for transportation of his family to England. At a salary of $14.60 a week, Elias built a highly satisfactory machine for corset-making in eight months. He collected no further money nor received proper recompense for the productive machine because of a falling-out with Thomas, an arrogant and high-handed man.

Out of work in a foreign country, Howe borrowed tools and, in a rented room, began to construct his fourth sewing machine. He shortly was forced, by financial circumstances, to send his wife and three children back to America. Broke and again in debt, he sold his fourth machine in England for less than twenty-five dollars. To satisfy creditors and pay his own steerage passage home, he pawned both his much-prized first sewing machine and his letters patent.

Misfortune was to be his for a little longer. Soon after his return to the United States, his wife died, and his motherless children were cared for by neighbors, devoted friends to Howe. A minor mishap was the loss of his household possessions in a shipwreck. Howe suffered another setback when his longtime partner Fisher sold his half interest in the sewing machine. Fortunately, George W. Bliss, the new partner, although not of Howe's own choosing, was enthusiastic about the commercial potential of the machine.

Howe was working as an odd-job machinist when he learned that his sewing machine was being made and marketed without royalty to him. Immediately, he decided to sue those infringing his patent. Bliss, while willing to lend Howe the money for legal fees, did insist on collateral. That was arranged by a mortgage on the farm of Elias Howe, Sr., whose faith in his son's invention never wavered.

While the suits proceeded through law courts, Howe made various kinds of sewing machines in his own small shop, established in New York City. At an 1851 fair there, he demonstrated a machine for sewing pantaloons, waistcoats and gaiters; his machine was bought by New York tailors, and other types were purchased by manufacturers of a variety of products. Several of one type of machine, ordered by a manufacturer in Worcester, Massachusetts, did the intricate and strong stitching of bootlegs, sewing the leather with precision and durability.

In court Howe triumphed over his competitors who, to a man, had infringed on his patent. Hunt, inventor of the 1834 lock-stitch machine, applied for his first patent in 1854, but was denied it because of his twenty-year lapse of interest. Oddly enough, the original Hunt model, disassembled, was found in a building on New York's Gold Street where Howe's workshop was located. When cleaned and repaired, Hunt's machine proved to be inoperable, although the basic design was good.

With a clear title to the patent of the first practical sewing machine, Howe became, in 1854, the sole owner as well.

Bliss died, and for a nominal fee Howe obtained the half interest his second partner had held.

Hunt was not the only loser when his machine was found to be inferior. Isaac M. Singer, the sewing-machine manufacturer against whom Howe had the strongest claim of infringement, had based his defense on Hunt's invention being earlier than Howe's. Singer paid Howe an outright $15,000 for infringement and, like other manufacturers of sewing machines, was ordered to pay Howe a royalty on every machine made.

Twenty-four manufacturers licensed to make sewing machines gathered at Albany, New York, in 1856, to protest infringement charges. When not one licensee was willing to chance public examination of his machine, the group collectively agreed to settlement out of court, as suggested by an astute and distinguished lawyer, George Gifford. Howe was awarded a royalty of five dollars on every sewing machine sold in the United States, and one dollar on every machine exported. After the renewal of Howe's patent in 1861, he received a royalty of one dollar on every sewing machine sold anywhere in the world.

Howe was generous with the fortune, so long anticipated, that he never doubted would come from his sewing machine. During the Civil War he served his country as manufacturer and soldier. He saw to it that 50,000 sandbags were shipped in less than a day after a War Department order was received. There could have been no profit for him from the rush job of cutting, sewing and packaging the bags within twenty-four hours. At his own expense Howe outfitted the Seventh Regiment of Connecticut, providing a horse for every officer. The men of the regiment, organized by Howe, elected him colonel; but he preferred to serve as a private, in spite of his slight physical handicap.

Howe retained a lively interest in his sewing machine until his death, at the age of forty-eight, in the fall of 1867. By then his original invention, capable of only straight stitching, was outmoded; Howe's latest models hemmed, embroidered, gathered, folded, braided, and could be adjusted to make buttonholes. The sewing machine had progressed far beyond even his optimistic hopes for it.

AND AFTER

American names linked with Howe's as important to the development of the sewing machine are Wilson, Gibbs and Singer.

Allen B. Wilson, a cabinetmaker, built his first sewing machine at Pittsfield, Massachusetts, and demonstrated it there in March, 1849. His third machine, in which he replaced a two-motion feed with a segmental screw device, he patented on August 12, 1851. His subsequent machines were distinguished by two devices: a rotary hook and a four-motion feed. The hook took the place of the shuttle; and the four-motion feed, adapted by all manufacturers, increased the maneuverability of the cloth being sewn.

The feed depended on a serrated bar moved by cams in a to-and-fro horizontal motion and an up-and-down vertical motion. The feeding bar moved up through an opening in the machine table, contacted the underside of the cloth, moved horizontally forward the length of the stitch, carrying the cloth along, and dropped from contact, releasing the cloth. The four-motion cycle then was repeated for the next stitch.

The only American sewing machine to come out of the South was invented by James A. E. Gibbs, a Virginia farmer. In 1855 he saw a picture of a sewing machine, but had no idea how the mechanism, not shown, produced its stitch. Gibbs patented a revolving hook for a chain-stitch machine that was named for him and a partner named Wilcox. Because his model incorporated Howe's eye-pointed needle and Wilson's four-motion feed, Gibbs paid a royalty of seven dollars on every one of the first machines he manufactured.

Isaac Morton Singer (1811–1875) was born in Pittstown, New York, and like Howe, left school at age twelve. Until he was nineteen, Singer worked as an unskilled laborer at Rochester, and for a few months was an apprentice to a machinist. For nine years afterward he moved around the country, always able to make a good living because of his mechanical ability. On May 16, 1839, while living in Lockport, Illinois, Singer took out his first patent; it was for a rock-drilling machine that he promptly sold, squandering the money. Ten years later, he patented a machine for carving both wood and metal, and went to New York to finance the construction. The carving machine, perfected within a year, was put into operation only a few days before the factory was completely destroyed by a boiler explosion. The plant accident left Singer penniless, and he took a job as machinist.

In 1851, the manager of the machine shop where Singer worked asked Singer's advice about the repairs of a customer's sewing machine, and said a fortune could be made by the inventor of a practical model. Like Howe, Singer was motivated to invention by his financial needs. In twelve hours he drew a rough sketch of a sewing machine that was completed in eleven days. Singer took out his patent on August 12, 1851, the same day that Wilson patented his machine with the segmental screw device.

Although he had to make substantial restitution to Howe for patent infringement, Singer's first machine was more than an adaptation of Howe's. The needle of the Singer sewing machine moved vertically, not horizontally; the handwheel was replaced by a treadle. Singer used the wheel-feed, an improvement on the baster-plate, and for holding cloth in place, a device like Thimonnier's presser-foot.

Singer was respected by his competitors, rival manufacturers with whom he arranged for a pooling of patents from which they all profited. Between 1851 and 1865, he personally patented twenty components for his sewing machines. Standard parts were interchangeable from factory to factory; customer training was available; inexpensive repair service was offered; and inventors were retained to produce new gadgets for increased uses of machines in homes and industry.

Singer was an imaginative inventor, a master mechanical craftsman, a creative businessman and an experienced showman, having briefly been in the theatrical profession as actor and as box-office manager. He promoted his machines by exhibitions at fairs, by contests, and by widespread advertising that made the word *Singer* synonymous with the term *sewing machine* throughout the world.

The typewriter radically changed office procedures, increased job opportunities, especially for women, and at last was approved for social correspondence.

CHRISTOPHER LATHAM SHOLES
1819–1890, American

Queen Anne of England issued the first patent for a writing machine to one Henry Mill, in the year 1714. In theory, Mill's machine was expected to prevent the alteration of public records and the counterfeiting of official documents; in practice, it was a curiosity of limited use. Mechanical substitutes for penmanship intrigued subsequent inventors concerned with the speed and legibility of writing, not with the falsification of a royal court's papers. More than a hundred years after the issuance of the patent to Mill, the first writing machine was patented in the United States, where the typewriter was to be invented and mass-manufactured, with improvements now continuing.

The first American writing machine, called the *typographer,* was invented by William Burt of Detroit, Michigan, whose patent application was approved in 1829 by President Andrew Jackson. That machine looked like a big wooden soapbox; its mechanism was set on a flat surface, and a lettered dial like a clockface depended for operation on a rather clumsy arm, or lever. Although well publicized, the Burt machine did not catch on. A so-called printing machine, the first to have a cylindrical carriage for holding the paper, was patented in 1843 by Charles Thurber of Worcester, Massachusetts. There followed, in 1850, a piano-keyboard machine invented by Oliver T. Eddy of Baltimore, Maryland, who for the first time used an inked ribbon instead of an inked roller for recording the letter impressions. In 1857, peg keys were introduced in a model designed by Dr. William Francis of New York.

A careful investigation of the first few American writing machines would have considerably lessened the laborious experimentation of the inventor of the first practical typewriter—Christopher Latham Sholes. He and his associates failed to study, in advance, the details of models previously patented, but subsequently Sholes adopted the best devices of several earlier machines.

Sholes was established as a Wisconsin state official, both by election and by appointment, and as a successful newspaper editor before he attempted any invention. All of his inventing efforts had to do with publishing, the trade he entered as an apprentice.

At fourteen, Christopher, a frail youngster, became a printer's devil at the *Intelligencer* in Danville, Pennsylvania, six miles from Mooresburg where he was born on Valentine's Day, 1819. In the course of his apprenticeship, he repaired presses and other machinery, tackled problems of inking and the hand-setting of type, became familiar with the economics of circulation and advertising, and even experienced the routines of delivery service. By the time Sholes was eighteen, he was an expert compositer whose well-rounded training on a small-town newspaper gave him a sound background in printing techniques and publishing operations.

Christopher went with his parents to Green Bay, Wisconsin, where as state printer he was responsible for the house journal of the territorial legislature. He took the manuscript to Philadelphia and supervised its printing; returning to Green Bay with the completed journal, Sholes was complimented on his accomplishment. He briefly worked on a Green Bay newspaper owned and edited by his brother Charles Sholes, and for a time ran another of his brother's papers at Madison. The younger Sholes started his own paper, the *Southport Telegraph,* in what is now Kenosha where, in 1843, he was appointed postmaster. Later he was a Kenosha County member of the Wisconsin Assembly. Recognized as a public-spirited citizen, Sholes actively worked in several anti-slavery groups, and was a founder of the short-lived Excelsior Church, dedicated to the cause of pure democracy.

Attracted by progressive practices in Milwaukee, a thriving city, Sholes moved there with his wife and their growing family; he had, in all, ten children: four daughters and six sons. Indefatigable in his profession and in public service, Sholes served two terms as state senator and was appointed Commissioner of Public Works in Milwaukee. Never robust, he managed somehow to keep up with a schedule of activities that would have exhausted many a healthier man.

In Milwaukee, he was first editor of the *News* and then of the *Sentinel* which, as was customary at the time, had a profitable job-printing department. A strike of newspaper compositers that threatened a shutdown of the newsroom and the presses led Sholes to his first attempt at invention. Seeking a way to set type by machinery, he experimented with type impressions made of wax, but the models were unworkable and Sholes shelved his drawings. Although his mechanical typesetter came to nothing, the attempt to design it gave Sholes the impetus for further inventions.

Always interested in efficiency of newspaper operation, Sholes early worked out a simple way to improve delivery service by printing the names of his subscribers on the margins of papers. In September, 1864, with a printer friend, Samuel W. Soulé, Sholes took out a patent on a paging machine. It was logical for him to turn again to Soulé for advice about a machine for the automatic stamping of numbers on tickets, coupons and blankbooks turned out by the job-printing department. Until then the numbers had been affixed by hand stamps.

Together, Sholes and Soulé constructed an automatic stamping machine, patenting their model in mid-November, 1866. The efficient numbering machine much impressed Carlos Glidden, another friend and himself an inventor of independent means. Glidden suggested to Sholes the construction of a machine to print letters and words as clearly and as accurately as the stamping machine struck off figures.

The following July, Sholes read an article about a writing machine that was exhibited in England at the London Society of Arts by its inventor, John Pratt, of Alabama. Sholes, certain that he could build a machine less complicated and more dependable, once more consulted with Soulé. Glidden, already predisposed toward a writing machine, was willing and able to finance the project.

The first typewriter model was patented by Sholes, Soulé and Glidden on June 23, 1868. Its heavy boxlike frame was constructed from a wooden kitchen table. At the suggestion of Soulé, the type bars were convergent; that design, first used in 1833 by Xavier Projean, of Marseille, may or may not have been known to the American inventors. Projean is credited, too, with the first manual keyboard on a writing machine.

The flat paper carriage of the first machine of the Wisconsin partners was fastened to the box, and the impression on its tissue-paper tape was made by the type bars underneath. There were two disadvantages to the operator: He could not see the writing as he tapped out the letters. And it was all but impossible to produce necessary alignment when the tape was replaced in the machine for additional writing.

Sholes's first model looked more like a musical instrument than a typewriter. Its piano keyboard, equipped with a spacer, had a first row of ivory keys, a second row of ebony ones. All the letters were capitals, placed in alphabetical sequence; the eight numbers were arranged in fours, even and uneven, with the capital letter "I" used for "one." The sole punctuation symbol was a period.

3 5 7 9 N O P Q R S T U V W X Y Z
2 4 6 8 . A B C D E F G H I J K L M

For the second model, patented a month after the first, Sholes adopted Thurber's platen, the cylindrical carriage. Paper was placed on the carriage which was rolled up for each new line; a ratchet moved the carriage a notch forward at every stroke of the key. Several previous machines had failed in their purpose for lack of an efficient inker. Sholes chose the inked ribbon used earlier by Eddy and by Dr. Francis. Although typewriter ribbons have been much improved through the years, the original style reproduced a clear letter when firmly struck by the type bar.

Revisions of the typewriter were made continuously for several years in an old mill located in a spit of land between the Milwaukee River and the Rock River Canal. Sholes had more free time for his invention because he had given up newspaper work to become collector of customs for Milwaukee. A number of the new designs worked out in the mill loft were turned over to Matthias Schwalbach, a professional model-maker, best known in the community for his construction of Milwaukee's clock towers. It was Schwalbach who persuaded Sholes to discard the piano keyboard with its flat keys of ivory and upper keys of ebony. Sholes replaced them with peg keys arranged in four rows like those on the machine of Dr. Francis; that system shortened the longitudinal range of the fingers of the operator.

Numerous experimental models were tested for Sholes by his friend Charles Weller, a court reporter. Weller made history with the test sentence, "Now is the time for all good men to come to the aid of the party," ever since a standard phrase for those trying out the touch of a new typewriter. When Sholes became comptroller of Milwaukee, he had a street-paving contract written on another of his typewriter models. Reputedly, that contract was the first official document to be typewritten.

Sholes and Soulé, encouraged by the enthusiastic Glidden, finally completed a model about which they were confident; and a third typewriter patent was taken out in August, 1871. One of the hundreds of typewritten letters sent by the partners to businessmen in many parts of the country was received by James Densmore, a Pennsylvania oilman. In immediate response, he inquired about investing in the new machine, and was given one fourth of the patent in return for paying all expenses incurred up to that time in producing models.

Densmore, inspecting the latest model, approved it only in principle, objectively spotting its defects. Soulé and Glidden were bought out, and Sholes and Densmore became sole holders of the patents, the latter advancing funds for continued experimentation. They built some thirty models, many of them with changes suggested by James O. Clephane, a prominent Washingtonian.

Clephane was the most famous shorthand reporter in the United States. During the Civil War he was private secretary to William H. Seward, Secretary of State, and afterward was in constant demand as shorthand reporter for important criminal trials and at congressional hearings. A friend to presidents, both Buchanan and Lincoln, Clephane was an energetic man with many business interests.

He cooperatively took on the testing of the Sholes models but, a ruthless critic, often damaged a machine by deliberate rough treatment. His destructive methods so exasperated the normally even-tempered Sholes that the inventor was opposed to submitting more test models to Clephane. Densmore realistically thought it an advantage to have the typewriter models tested by an expert before manufacture was attempted. Guided by the advice of Clephane, the partners strengthened levers and rods, eased the tension of the spacer, loosened an inker too stiff in operation, and made other changes to increase ease and efficiency of operation.

Satisfied by a typewriter model completed in 1872, Sholes and Densmore retained an expert adviser on manufacture, George N. Yost, a master mechanic and supersalesman. He tested the model, suggested certain minor changes, and agreed with the partners that the typewriter was ready for the consideration of a manufacturer. His choice was E. Remington and Sons, at Ilion, New York.

Densmore and Yost took the Sholes model to the Remingtons, well-known makers of arms, and also manufacturers of farm implements and sewing machines. Eliphalet Remington, the founder, had been dead for more than a decade, and his son Philo was the member of the family who undertook the production of the typewriter. William J. Jenne headed the Remington technical group which, in March, 1873, began work on a machine that was marketable by the following September.

The Sholes model looked like a shark's head, the keys being the lower teeth, and the huge metal plate slanted inward above the keyboard being the big upper jaw. The small carriage was set at the very back of the machine's flat-surfaced top.

The redesign of the keyboard was a major feature of the Remingtons' first commercial typewriter. The company's mechanics abandoned the alphabetical and numerical orders of arrangement of keys so that those characters most frequently used were closest to the center of the machine. The operator still could not see the written words without swinging up the carriage. The typewriter was mounted on a table-high metal frame like the base of an early sewing machine, which the whole contraption much resembled, having as it did a floor-level foot pedal for returning the carriage to position after completion of a type line.

The type bars, jointed and made of wood, were set in pivots around a horizontal ring. The shorter arm of each bar was attached by wire to a lever ending in a letter of the keyboard. When the operator tapped a key, the activated type lifted, striking a single point on the platen, a rubber cylinder. Inked ribbon, wound on spools at either side of the machine, was between the type and the platen, which automatically moved to the left one space at each release of the keys.

The success of the first commercial typewriter spurred manufacturing by other companies and accelerated such improvements as an automatic ribbon reverse; carbon ribbon in place of inked ribbon; lock at the margin edge; margin release; increased number of keys; the addition of a decimal tabulating system.

Densmore and Sholes made separate business contracts with the Remington company. The farsighted financier, opting for royalty, ultimately realized a million and a half dollars from the typewriter.

Sholes sold his interest outright to Remington for twelve thousand dollars. With two sons he continued to design typewriter models, turning over to Remington, for additional payments, simplifications and improvements. The *Sholes Visible* permitted the operator to see not only a single line being written but the whole page of typing. The shift key, making possible the typing of upper- and lower-case letters, was added to the typewriter in 1878, the year that Sholes took out his last patent.

The inventor was ever after in failing health; a consumptive, he spent nine years vainly trying to find the climate ideal for a tubercular. Feeble and wasted, Sholes died five days after his seventy-first birthday in 1890, the year the Remington company introduced the first typewriter model with an eighty-four-character keyboard. The invention of Sholes was to become a practical machine of common use in business and the home, by the secretary, the social correspondent, the professional writer and the student.

AND AFTER

The first teletypewriter, put into service in 1904, was an electromechanical device operated by a start-stop system, transmitting from a remote point to a receiving machine. Each key of the teletypewriter produces a combination of impulses that activate a receiving key. There are seven impulses for each character to be recorded: one is the start, two through six represent the character, and seven is the stop. The machine, making only capital letters, punctuation marks and numbers, is used by newspaper wire services, for stock-market ticker tape, and for weather reports in letter code. The teletypewriter records on tape or page machines, either separately or simultaneously, depending on the requirements.

Accelerating type bars that reduced friction drag represented a major and improved feature of a visible writing machine offered for sale in 1906. The 1908 typewriter called the *Noiseless,* a commercial misnomer, actually was somewhat quieter than the standard-action manual, but the grasshopper-stroke type bar of the *Noiseless* never gained general acceptance.

Electric typewriters were not mass-produced until after World War II, although experimental models dated back to 1872 when Thomas A. Edison patented the first. And in 1934 the International Business Machines Corporation made the *Electromatic,* based on a model bought from another company; electricity moved the type bars and the carriage return. IBM's *Selectric* of 1961 was designed on the mechanical principle of late nineteenth-century writing machine models: the type faces were grouped on single units that moved across a stationary platen. The *Selectric's* typing element, replacing the type bars, resembles a globe; the globe crosses the stationary carrier of the paper.

An electric typewriter does not require the expenditure of as much effort as the manual, with the result that a typist is less tired at the end of a workday; and the electrically powered machine reduces the incidence of backache, an occupational complaint of authors who spend hours of every day at the keyboard.

Copies of letters that appeared to be originals were first made possible by the Hooven *Automatic Typer,* a machine designed on the principle of the player piano. Letter code was punched into an endless paper roll, its perforations activating typewriter keys. That automatic machine was superseded by more efficient designs and other types of copying devices.

The single-system automatic-typing unit of the *Royaltyper* combines manual and automatic typing, tape techniques (reading, punching and reproduction), and does away with proofreading. An operator can do 125 letters a day on one *Royaltyper,* 500 letters on four machines simultaneously operating.

There is an electronic typewriter that produces 1,800 characters a second; another is capable of typing in fifty languages. Many machines, even portable, have individual language keyboards, representing the letters and punctuation symbols of the languages of China, Japan, Israel, Greece, Persia, India, and other countries. It is possible to get a machine with one hundred kinds of type face, and another with a justifier to make the right-hand margin even, like that of a printed line. Braille keyboards make Braille copy, which is very much like the embossed writing of a Beach model, 1856, and a Foucault, 1849, both writing machines that were unusable for any but the blind. Typewriters activated, operated and programmed by calculating machines and computers are presently proliferating in proportion to the acceleration of the techniques of automation.

Designs essential for the advancement of man-in-flight were made by Langley, whose first scientific studies were focused on space.

SAMUEL PIERPONT LANGLEY
1834–1906, American

Through a shift of professional interests in his middle age, Samuel Langley became a phenomenon among scientific investigators: already a distinguished astronomer, he turned to the development of heavier-than-air craft, establishing an unprecedented link between two apparently unrelated research objects. The solar studies in his first career were essential for the manned space flights that were to be extensions of aeronautic experimentation, his second career.

By birth and circumstance, Langley was conditioned to be an astronomer. Born into a family of New England settlers, he had a number of ancestors who were prominent intellectuals. One of those, Increase Mather, a Puritan clergyman, author and president of Harvard College, wrote in 1683 a paper on comets which is accepted as the first American publication on any astronomical subject.

Astronomy was one of the many and varied interests of Samuel's father, a wholesale merchant. The elder Langley encouraged his sons, Samuel and John, to scan the night skies with the family's small telescope which, by day, was often focused on the sights of Boston. Samuel, who remembered reading works on astronomy at only nine, started construction of the first of several refractor telescopes when he was about twenty.

His formal education ended with his graduation from Boston High School, where he excelled in mathematics. At school and at home, he engaged in projects requiring aptitude for drawing and for the execution of mechanical designs. Those talents he used while employed, first with an architectural firm in Boston and, later, in the offices of architects of St. Louis and Chicago.

Deciding that architecture was not the career for him, Samuel returned home in 1864 and, with his younger brother again as willing assistant, began the construction of a large reflector telescope. They set up a workshop in their barn and, by making every piece of equipment for their telescope, learned as much as possible about optics and developed expertise as instrument-makers. It took the self-taught brothers three years of tedious trial and error to complete their telescope, which had a silvered-glass mirror instead of the polished-metal mirror commonly used in American-made telescopes.

After an 1865 European tour of cultural centers and historic sights, the brothers continued their collaboration on construction of the telescope. By the time it was finished, Samuel was working at the Harvard College Observatory. From there he went to Annapolis, Maryland, as an assistant professor of mathematics at the United States Naval Academy, where he supervised the reactivation of the astronomical observatory, which had not been in operation during the Civil War.

In 1867, Langley was appointed Professor of Astronomy and Physics at the Western University of Pennsylvania (now the University of Pittsburgh) and Director of the University's Allegheny Observatory, situated on the Ohio River. The observatory was in every way ill equipped for research and investigative projects. Its poorly constructed thirteen-inch telescope was in no way comparable to the larger instrument that Langley had built, making it precision perfect for scientific observation by professional astronomers.

Undaunted, Langley took charge of the Allegheny Observatory, slowly equipping it with essential instruments, assembling a suitable library where there had been none, and establishing funds for astronomical observation field trips. With imagination and enterprise, he devised a profitable operation that made the observatory largely self-supporting. Synchronization of clocks and other timepieces was not then dependable, and Langley offered to railroads a much-needed accurate time service. The Pennsylvania Railroad was the first to subscribe to the Allegheny service, which began in 1870. Twice a day, correct time signals based on astronomical observations were transmitted to telegraph offices at about three hundred railroad stations. The money-making service attracted other customers eager for standardization of time, among them watchmakers, industrial companies and city governments.

Langley, efficient at organization and proficient at fundraising, was creative and orderly in his astronomical investigations and research. He concentrated on solar studies, examining the sun's formation, its gases and spots, and the spectrum. His previous experience in instrument-making and in drafting for architects proved invaluable. He made astronomical sketches that were both beautiful and dependable. A drawing of a sunspot he did in 1873 was a standard textbook illustration until twentieth-century photography produced exact and detailed pictures of sunspots.

In an original approach to astronomy, Langley favored a concept of the physical composition of planetary bodies rather than that of their positions and movements in the firmament. The physical aspects of astronomical objects were also emphasized by the physicist Edward C. Pickering (who in 1872 became Director of the Harvard College Observatory) and by a few other scientists with advanced views. Their "new astronomy" is the present-day astrophysics.

For his thorough study of the sun's spectrum, Langley needed an instrument for detecting and measuring heat present in the absorption lines. He designed and built, almost without help, the bolometer, a device for studying heat distribution in the solar spectrum.

Well aware that effective solar energy study had to be made as far as possible above sea level, Langley organized an ambitious field trip to California's towering Mt. Whitney, 14,495 feet high. The expedition was chiefly underwritten by a philanthropist friend of Langley's, William Thaw; some equipment was provided by United States Army meteorologists in the research group. In the summer of 1881, ladened with camp supplies and with thousands of pounds of essential instruments, members of the expedition climbed from the Mojave Desert to observation points on Mt. Whitney. Clean and clear air at every level facilitated research.

The expedition was rewarding for all of the scientific observers and experimenters. Langley's bolometer produced remarkable results, and with it he discovered an unknown extension of the spectrum's infrared area, never before seen. To his surprise he was able to continue observation of the extension at the Allegheny Observatory in spite of the murkiness at its low-altitude location, only 400 feet above sea level. The resultant mapping of the extension was one of Langley's important contributions to the science of astronomy.

In 1886, Langley turned his attention to flight in heavier-than-air craft. Ever a man to put first things first, Langley assembled salient facts about requisite power before attempting to design a machine for flight. Typically, he began his experimentation at the drawing board, designing an elaborate whirling table for aerodynamic research. The sixty-foot-diameter table, when constructed on the observatory grounds, was placed in a fenced enclosure to prevent operational interference by winds.

A steam engine, installed underground, provided power through a shaft connected to the table. Two thirty-foot arms, made of wood, rotated at speeds up to seventy miles per hour; recording devices were attached to the tips of the arms. In Langley's 1891 report *Experiments in Aerodynamics*, he concluded that high-speed flight "is not only possible but within reach of mechanical means which we now possess."

The report on aerodynamics was published by the Smithsonian Institution, of which Langley became Secretary in 1887. He ably served as a progressive administrator of the Institution while, at the same time, he continued his own scientific research. His first flight models, powered by rubber bands, looked like playthings. Onlookers must have been amused by the sight of the stately and distinguished Secretary flipping his tiny models into the air. Dozens of variations of the basic design were tried with a lack of success. Flight, if it could be called that, was short in time and distance. No matter what the wing structures or propeller types, the models remained airborne for only a few seconds.

Langley, deciding to try larger models powered by steam, called the first one he designed the "Aerodrome No. 0." On paper, it had a light frame-metal hull, five feet long and ten inches wide; two sets of wings, a pair forward being larger than the pair at the tail; two steam engines, together weighing four pounds, capable of producing one horsepower; and two pusher propellers, each thirty inches in diameter, to be driven by steam through shafts. Early in production, the model was proved to be impractical, as it might not have been today. But it was to be more than half a century before the inception of essential technical advances: miniaturization, the production of lightweight metals, the development of synthetics, and the availability of stronger power from sources less heavy.

Langley's first model was cumbersome and overweight; its engines, which gave about half as much steam as estimated, precariously vibrated. Pressure contorted the fragile wings. Like Aerodrome No. 0, No. 1, No. 2 and No. 3 were scrapped in the workshop; finally No. 4 looked like a possibility for flight. In the spring of 1893, having earlier decided to test his models over water, Langley optimistically positioned a launching vessel in a Potomac River lagoon, close to Quantico, Virginia. In principle, the planned launch into the wind was patterned on the takeoff of birds; in theory, if a model fell during over-water flight, it would be less damaged than by impact on hard ground.

The boat for launching was a scow, 12 feet by 38 feet long, on which a superstructure was raised. The interior was a floating workshop for storage, assemblage and minor repairs. Atop the roof, there was a launch platform dominated by a starting device, a hinged rod designed to give the model velocity and direction on takeoff.

A series of attempted launches of No. 4 began in the fall of 1893. All were fiascoes. Langley, preparing for future trials, replaced the launch rod with a catapult, and equipped the model with larger engines powered by gasoline instead of alcohol. On an October day in 1894, No. 4 and No. 5 were aboard the launching vessel. The former, on its test, fell into the Potomac and was buoyed by an air-filled canister installed for just such an emergency. Immediately after the recovery of No. 4, No. 5, a single-engine model, was launched and slid tail-first into the water, after a flight of three seconds in time and thirty-five feet in distance.

An ingenious check of wing strength by weighting the wings with sand, in weight equivalent to the model's, proved that the wings were not strong enough to do the job for which they were designed. Under the weight of the sand, the wings buckled to a degree that accounted for the malfunction. A design of two sets of identical wings of equal area—one set forward, the other aft—was adopted.

On May 6, 1896, Aerodrome No. 6 was damaged at launch. In midafternoon, No. 5 was launched and flew. Langley, after years of patient experimentation, could admit to success. About it he wrote: "For never in any part of the world or in any period had any machine of man's construction sustained itself in the air for even half of this brief time.

"Still the aerodrome went on in a rising course until, at the end of a minute and a half (for which time only it was provided with fuel and water), it had accomplished a little over half a mile. Now it settled rather than fell into the river with a gentle descent.

"It was immediately taken out and flown again with equal success. There was nothing to indicate that it might not have flown indefinitely except for the limit put upon it."

The trial flight was observed by Langley's longtime friend Dr. Alexander Graham Bell, who insisted that the Smithsonian's Secretary must formally report to scientists on the successful flights. Langley made the announcement to the French Academy and, in a popular article, let the world know that his experimentations in what he called *aerodromics* were finished. It was Langley's sincere intention that others should go forward with "the commercial and practical developments of the ideas." He meant what he wrote, but in the same article he observed that tactical warfare of the future might be changed by air flights. That statement was later to be responsible for his own return to aeronautical invention.

After the start of the Spanish-American War in the spring of 1898, President William McKinley asked Langley to initiate experimentation with a military aircraft large enough to carry a man. Like many another patriot, the Secretary of the Smithsonian felt it impossible to refuse a call for his services from the government of his country. He agreed, however reluctantly, to accept the challenge, putting aside valid reasons for refusal: the demands of his position at the Smithsonian, his own age and health.

The first matter for consideration was the power source for a manned vehicle. Patently steam power was no longer feasible, and internal combustion engines were not readily available; mass production was very much in the future. Langley approached several manufacturers, specifying the need for an internal combustion engine capable of producing . . . "at least 12 horsepower." Contracting for a second engine, after a first order had not worked out, Langley made arrangements for going forward with the Army Board of Ordnance and Fortification. The War Department put up $50,000 to finance the project, for which Langley received no remuneration; in time, the Smithsonian supplied $20,000 for completion of the work.

Langley, ever methodical, wasted no time while awaiting delivery of the engine on order. He rebuilt Aerodromes No. 5 and No. 6 for use in testing a new launching device, underneath the air machine instead of overhead. The support system below proved to be efficient when the aerodrome models were catapulted from the launching vessel early in 1899.

When the engine was not ready by its promised delivery date, Langley ordered work on the flight vehicle to be stopped and began construction of a one-eighth scale model. He planned to use it to test the stability of the design, by sending it up like a kite from the mast of a small boat. Just before launch, the mast snapped and the one-eighth scale model, toppling into the water, sank, never to be recovered.

Charles M. Manly, a technician of outstanding ability, served as Langley's right hand on the manned-flight program. For several years the two colleagues concerned themselves with acquiring the ideal internal combustion engine. Manly designed and ground-tested a large engine which, with all its parts, weighed 187 pounds and could produce more than 52 horsepower. He also made a one-quarter scale model of the manned vehicle, powering it with a gasoline engine. That model made aeronautic history in 1901 by completing the first flight of any heavier-than-air craft powered by a gasoline engine.

Langley and Manly, his master mechanic, endured with fortitude delays and disappointments, setbacks and failures. Taking two steps forward for every one lost, they finally had the aerodrome ready for testing at the Smithsonian workshop. The structure, fabric coverings, large parts and small components were minutely checked for durability, stress capability, vibration factor, efficiency potential.

At the insistence of Langley, launching was to be consistent with those of the satisfactorily completed flights of the unmanned Aerodromes No. 5 and No. 6, which were catapulted from the glorified houseboat and were airborne over water. Manly, who wanted to launch from shore or from water surface, had no choice but to give in to the Secretary's wishes. By persistence, Manly did obtain permission to be test pilot of the aerodrome. Langley, who intended from the first to make unmanned preliminary tests with ballast in the aerodrome equal in weight to that of a man, conceded to Manly in spite of the obvious physical hazards.

On July 14, 1903, a specially built launching vessel was anchored in the Potomac at a site forty miles from Washington. The shed of the sixty-by-forty-foot flatboat was dwarfed by its skeletal superstructure. Affixed to the roof was a fifteen-ton turntable for maneuvering an overhead launching platform. It was centered by a catapult track, five feet wide and eighty-five feet long, on which at launch time, the aerodrome would hover like a giant bird.

Workmen inside the launch shed made adjustments and final inspections of Manly's one-quarter scale model and of the aerodrome that Manly was to pilot. An August launch of the fifty-eight-pound model was so successful that the aerodrome was raised to the catapult track on September 3. It proved not to be operative. Dampness had affected the dry cell batteries and the glue along the wing ribs.

With repairs completed and weather favorable, a launch was scheduled for October 7. The aerodrome was placed on the track, which was to be positioned in takeoff direction, against the wind, by the turntable. The steel-framed aerodrome weighed 850 pounds, which included the 187-pound engine with essential auxiliary components. Twin propellers were seven feet in diameter. The four wings, their wooden ribs cloth-covered, each measured, from plane frame to tip, twenty-two and one-half feet. One pair was set forward of the pilot's car, the second set aft. Inside the car there were two wheels to the pilot's right. He was to use one wheel to control the tail, which was not rigidly set, and the other for manipulation of the steering rudder. The complexities of the instrument panel of any modern aircraft demonstrate the advance of aeronautics since 1903 when Manly had to flight-check only a single instrument, a tachometer for monitoring the performance by the engine that was capable of an average of 950 r.p.m. A wooden seat, set on shock-absorbing sponge rubber, was placed lengthwise in the cabin which was five feet long, three wide.

Manly stepped into the pilot's car at noon on October 7.

He wore goggles, a life preserver, a cotton shirt and work pants. A barometer for recording the height of ascent was sewn to the knee section of his left trouser leg.

Rockets signaled the launch of the aerodrome which, at takeoff, was sixty feet above the Potomac. The craft sharply plunged toward the water, and Manly's efforts to use the cockpit control wheels were ineffective. He crashed with the aerodrome and, surfacing, swam to a portion of the wreckage that was exposed above the water surface. The press, gathered for the momentous launch, badgered Manly into making an immediate statement about the flight failure. He said that it seemed to be from lack of balance. In a formal statement the following day, Langley explained that instability was not the reason for the crash. There had been some difficulty with the launch track, which had not properly released the aerodrome. Langley was convinced of the flight potential of the aerodrome, and, reconditioned, it was ready for another test by December 8.

The launch vessel, moved to Washington after the July mishap, was towed from its 8th Street slip to the Potomac Flats in late afternoon. Dusk was settling over the river when Manly again was launched from the top of the houseboat. He felt the aerodrome vibrate violently as it took off at a steep rise. Again his attempts to use the controls of rudder and tail were futile; the mechanisms did not respond. The aerodrome plummeted, top down, into the water. Manly was lucky to get out of the crash alive: He freed himself from the wreckage by yanking apart his jacket, entangled in the framework. Swimming away from the submerged section of the plane, he tried to surface and banged his head against ice. Diving, he swam underwater for some distance and then, fortunately, rose through an opening in the partly frozen river.

The cause of the second accident was not definitely determined, although a section of the tail did drag and collapse shortly before the actual takeoff. Of all the photographs taken late on that winter's day of 1903, only one came out. It showed severe damage to the rear set of wings and slight damage to the right front wing. The aerodrome was mutilated even more during the salvage operation, following which the battered and misshapen vehicle was returned to the Smithsonian.

The press immediately made Langley the subject of ridicule in written words and by cartoons. It was a sad and bitter experience for a man who, in the first years of his experimentation in aerodromics, systematically informed the general public by popular articles and through lectures in layman language of the progress being made in flight research. For more than seventeen years he was inventive in the design of airborne vehicles, himself building some flight models and directing the construction of others. The extent and value of his research were known to scientists of his own country and abroad through the widely circulated publications of the Smithsonian Institution, which contained his own detailed reports of his scientific experimentation in aerodromics. Less was known about the specifics of the man-in-flight program because, in writing, Langley had assured the Army Board of Ordnance and Fortification that, for reasons of national security, "privacy would be observed with regard to this work."

His contribution to the science of aeronautics, to manned aircraft, and even to manned space flight has long since been recognized and acknowledged. In his honor the first aircraft carrier was christened the USS *Langley* in 1922. A major division headquarters of the National Aeronautics and Space Administration is the Langley Research Center at Langley Air Force Base, in Virginia.

AND AFTER

Only nine days after the ill-fated test of the manned aerodrome designed by Langley, airborne men flew at Kitty Hawk, North Carolina. The day was December 17, 1903. The pilots were Wilbur and Orville Wright, designers of the airplane.

The Wright brothers were master mechanics whose business was the repair and building of bicycles. Their interest in flying was sparked in the 1890's by glider experiments conducted by two German brothers, Otto and Gustav Lilienthal. The former, an aeronautical engineer, was the author of books on aviation well known to the Wright brothers, who avidly read all aeronautical reports, including Langley's *Experiments in Aerodynamics*.

In his small factory at Dayton, Ohio, Wilbur Wright (1867–1912) built a model biplane with a five-foot wingspread. This was flown as a kite, succeeding as Langley's model testing by kite principle did not.

Progressing to gliders, the Wrights experimented with designs for man-carrying types. On advice of weather experts, they chose as their test site Kill Devil Hill, near Kitty Hawk. The highest sandhill at the Atlantic Ocean beach was 100 feet above sea level. From there, the first tests of a Wright-built glider were made in late September, 1900.

With the pilot in horizontal position to cut down wind resistance, controlled glides of 300 feet were completed in wind at 27 m.p.h.

Back in Dayton, Orville Wright (1871–1948) constructed an eight-foot-long wind tunnel with a passage eighteen inches square. Wind was produced by power from a gasoline engine. Testing more than 200 wing and biplane combinations in the tunnel, the brothers studied lift, drag and center of pressure.

By 1902, the Wright brothers were ready for test flights of a newly designed glider with a vertical steering rudder. They sent it through 1,000 glides, some of them of more than 600 feet. Several flights in early 1903 were of more than a minute's duration in high winds.

Otto Lilienthal's gliders depended for stability on the shifting weight of the pilot. From long and meticulous study of wing performance and structure, the Wright brothers learned that position correction in flight was more effectively achieved by manipulation of movable portions of the wings. Their airplane launched in 1903 was equipped with a device for gaining latent lateral balance by warping the wing tips to decrease lift at either side.

There was a vertical steering rudder behind the plane and an elevator, or horizontal, rudder ahead of the machine. Two chain-driven airscrews turned in opposite directions to prevent imbalance. Instead of wheels, there were landing skids in front of the main wings. The land launch was by catapult; the plane, on a monorail, had a towline with a falling weight to give momentum at takeoff.

The 750-pound machine had a 12-horsepower engine

capable of 31 m.p.h. It had four horizontal cylinders of four-inch bore and four-inch stroke. The pilot stretched flat on his stomach beside the motor.

At ten thirty in the morning of December 17, 1903, Orville Wright piloted the first flight of 120 feet in 12 seconds. Two flights followed. Then at noon, Wilbur Wright piloted a flight of 852 feet in 59 seconds.

Although a wind accident irreparably damaged the plane after its fourth flight, the Wright brothers were not discouraged. They continued to build airplanes and, as pioneer pilots, both established flight records. After official acceptance of their airplane in 1909, they produced machines for military use, under contract to the United States government.

Man was at last in flight, and airplane manufacturing boomed in the United States and Europe.

Less than twenty-seven years after the record-making flights at Kitty Hawk, another milestone in aviation was marked by Frank Whittle in England. At the age of twenty-two, he filed for the first jet engine patent in January, 1930.

Sir Frank Whittle, now a retired Air Commander of the Royal Air Force, was an RAF apprentice, then attended the RAF engineering school and Cambridge University, by arrangement with the RAF. At nineteen, while still at the engineering school, he wrote a thesis containing advanced theories on rocket propulsion and gas turbine engines.

The design of Whittle's engine was for the power of a full-scale aircraft. It was to be eleven years after he filed for patent that his jet airplane would be tested. In the meantime, Frank Whittle had setbacks that would have disheartened a less determined man. Because the RAF did not classify the engine design, its specifics were published in numerous journals. And, at the time of patent renewal, the young inventor was unable to pay the five-pound fee. His finances soon after improved. He became a flying instructor for the RAF, then a test pilot for an aircraft experimental research center before being attached to Power Jets, Ltd. There he concentrated on the development of gas turbines for jet-propulsion aircraft.

Doggedly carrying forward his project, Whittle found increasing interest in his turbojet engine with its single-stage centrifugal compressor, turbine, combustion chamber and propelling nozzles. Air from the atmosphere, compressed inside the engine to several times its original pressure by the heat of fuel combustion, jetted out to spin compression rotors that reacted on inflowing air.

In August, 1939, an order was placed with the Gloster Aircraft Company for an airframe to be powered by a turbojet engine. The engine, capable of 16,000 r.p.m., was installed in the frame, and the aircraft was ready for testing on May 15, 1941. The first British jet-propulsion unit was satisfactory in performance and, after further development, the engine type was installed in the Gloster Meteor fighter of World War II.

American air officers, invited to inspect Whittle's jet following its test flight, recommended to their government the immediate production of jet fighters in the United States. Since World War II, jets of everincreasing size, range and speed have rendered standard-engine airplanes almost obsolete, particularly for military purposes and for commercial use by global travel airlines.

Two men produced internal combustion engines to implement their individual plans for the assured future of the horseless carriage.

KARL BENZ
1844–1929, German

GOTTLIEB DAIMLER
1834–1900, German

Controversy about the invention of the automobile is common because of the lack of standards of evaluation. A theorist is credited in one country and, in another, a mechanical expert. But even proponents of favorite sons, or fellow countrymen, agree that the automobile was given impetus by two developers of the internal combustion engine: Karl Benz and Gottlieb Daimler.

Both Germans, they experimented concurrently but, in every sense of the word, independently. The eventual merger of their two companies was not until four decades after Benz and Daimler separately produced self-propelled vehicles and twenty-six years after Daimler's death. Consistent with conflicting claims over horseless carriages, there is continuing disagreement over which man made the most significant pioneering contribution to the automobile as we know it today.

Recognition is due both men who, admittedly, were poles apart in approach and action. Benz, a loner at the drawing board, for years spent solitary hours in deep thought about engines for road vehicles. A conservative, he was resistant to change even when its advisability was evident to others. It was not his nature to venture far from his workshop or, later, from his factory. Daimler, an enthusiastic innovator, was the originator and adapter of new concepts and manufacturing procedures. He traveled and briefly worked in various countries of Europe, communicating and associating with other automotive engineers, men interested in automobiles, motorboats and airplanes.

Before Karl Benz was twelve, he excelled in science studies and, when barely in his teens, became assistant to his school's physics instructor. The pupil's duties were primarily to assemble and to arrange equipment for class experiments. At home, Karl had a makeshift chemical laboratory that doubled as darkroom. Photography was more than a hobby because, on school holidays, he made pin money by taking pictures of people and places in the Black Forest, where ancestors had been clockmakers. Young Benz also augmented the meager income of his widowed mother by repairing clocks and watches of their neighbors.

While a student in the Polytechnic of Karlsruhe, he was influenced by a distinguished teacher who was an authority on engines. When Benz was twenty-one, he quit the engineering school to take a job with an engine construction company. At the end of exhausting twelve-hour workdays, he made sketches of horseless carriages and engines to power them, keeping to a rigid self-imposed schedule that left him few hours for sleep. Intent on obtaining practical design experience, Benz went to Mannheim and found employment with a manufacturer of wagons, cranes and pumps.

Not long after, he started his own one-man business on a back street of Mannheim. In a modest rented workshop he designed and made small two-stroke engines, primarily used for driving pumps. He was newly married and nearly broke when a silent partner made expansion possible. Benz began to build higher-powered engines, incorporating an air and gas pump of his design. A surface carburetor vaporized the fuel, and the entry of the gas into the cylinder was controlled by a slide valve. The internal combustion engines were so efficient in operation that Benz was unable to fill orders from local manufacturers.

With willing investors, Benz formed the Mannheim Gas Engine Company and branched out into larger manufacturing space, employing a machine-shop staff of forty. Failing to interest his partners in allocating surplus funds for the design of a horseless carriage, Benz had no choice but to experiment in secret, again after hours. His drawing-board progress in the design of an engine for running vehicles did not impress the associates of Benz and, dissolving the partnership, he returned to his original workshop.

Max Rose, a merchant of Mannheim, offered financial backing to Benz with the understanding that stationary gas engines were to be the chief products of manufacture. Although personally unenthusiastic about the horseless carriage, Rose was not opposed to Benz's experimentation with the design of an engine to power a road vehicle. Benz, Rose, and Wilhelm Esslinger formed Benz et Cie in the fall of

1883. The small company prospered, and Benz was able to go forward with practical plans for building a road vehicle.

He was prepared for the task ahead by concentrated thinking over two decades during which he had discarded hundreds of sketches for horseless carriage engines and dozens of drawings of vehicle frames. His stationary engines were driven by vaporized benzine, the same fuel Benz intended to use for his automobile. The engine, necessarily lighter in weight but capable of higher speed, was to be a four-stroke type adaptable to continual changes of speed. In 1884 he produced the first Benz internal combustion engine with slide valve and electric ignition. When a belt-operated dynamo proved unsatisfactory for ignition, Benz refined his original ignition system of cells, an induction coil and an uncomplicated commutator or rotary switch.

The first car's frame was a tricycle made of boiler tubes. A very large flywheel and the engine at the rear of the vehicle were placed in horizontal position. Motor-cooling was by natural circulation of water in a small tank above the engine; that general system was retained on Benz cars for many years. Two rear wheels, wire with solid rubber tires, moved on a solid axle to which elliptical rear springs were fixed. The small front wheel was without springs. Drive, from the countershaft with a built-in differential gear, went to the rear wheels by chains and sprockets. Steering by a central steering column was effected by a link, pinion, and rack. The driving belt ran from a loose pulley to a fixed one.

The design was remarkable for the time and for a man who was not in touch with others doing similar experimentation. But imperfections in operation and components showed up in the first test. On a spring day in 1885, Benz climbed onto the vehicle, sat down on a wooden box and took hold of the small wheel at the top of the central steering column.

Benzine was poured into the carburetor, water into the tank above the engine, and workmen pulled at the horizontal flywheel to start the single-cylinder engine built for a maximum speed of about 250 r.p.m. The engine was no sooner started than it stopped, stalled by the running of the belt from the loose to the fixed pulley. The engine needed speed to operate. Following a few abortive attempts to spark the motor, workmen pushed the vehicle, restarting the engine.

Benz, making history, drove the first car powered by an internal combustion engine. After completing a few random circles of the cinder track outside the workshop, the car again stopped. A broken ignition wire was repaired, and the proud designer, cheered by his wife and workmen, steered his car around and around the yard until a broken chain brought the first test to its conclusion.

Before an autumn demonstration to which friends and relatives were invited, numerous minor changes were made on the automobile. Stronger side chains replaced the original ones. The engine was dismantled for the installation of an improved mounting for the battery. A seat for the driver and one passenger was installed by a carriage-builder, and the frame was painted.

Frau Benz took the seat beside her husband; and their two sons, Eugen, then twelve, and Richard, ten, stood with the invited spectators. The engine did not respond to the swing of the flywheel, so with the belt worked onto the fixed pulley, workmen again pushed the vehicle. Instead of driving out onto the public road as he intended, Benz, paying less attention to his steering than to the sound of the motor, found himself headed for the brick wall surrounding the workshop yard. He pulled the side lever which controlled the single brake, but to no avail. Benz and his wife escaped injury in the crash of metal against brick, but the front of the vehicle was severely damaged.

Within a week the front wheel, steering column and twisted frame were repaired. The next trial run, on a public street but without prior announcement, lasted a few minutes in which the automobile traveled 100 yards. In a subsequent test the vehicle ran nonstop for one kilometer, at twelve kilometers per hour. The designer's goal was reached by an automobile with its engine of one horsepower, lying on its side; an inadequate brake; one speed and no radiator. The vehicle did have three features of today's automobile: an electric ignition, a differential gear and a water-cooling system.

Improvements were soon made on the systems of steering and braking. A second speed was added for driving up inclines. And Benz patented a carburetor with a supply pipe that was partly glass for checking on the amount of fuel present. Horsepower was gradually increased.

The first sale of a Benz car was made to Emile Roger of France in 1887, the year that Benz showed one of his automobiles at the Paris Exhibition, without creating any general interest. Primarily through proper promotion, carefully planned, he had better success at the 1888 Munich Imperial Exhibition, where he won a gold medal. His cars were in such demand that he had fifty workmen in his factory by 1889, when he exhibited again in Paris. There he took for a drive Emile Levassor, later a business associate of Daimler's.

With new partners and larger manufacturing facilities at another location, Benz built his first four-wheel automobile in 1890. But Benz cars became outmoded. The designer, stubborn about change, held to the principle of the horizontal engine and belt drive, and long refused to place the engine at the front of his cars. As a concession to the buying public, a front hood was installed, but it was only a cover to the repositioned water tank.

As late as 1905, Frau Benz and her husband drove around Mannheim in vintage cars, early models from the Benz factory. That year, Benz, pressured by his associates, finally permitted drastic design changes that led to extensive export to foreign countries and to outstanding records in racing by cars built at Benz et Cie. Benz himself was never enthusiastic about the updated models, even when the company prospered and expanded.

The father of Gottlieb Daimler wanted his son to take a job at the municipal office of his hometown, Schorndorf. But the boy, interested in mechanics to the exclusion of all other subjects, chose instead to become a gunmaker's apprentice. Although it was quickly obvious to the youth that a gunshop was not a stepping-stone to a career in engineering, he was a conscientious and able worker. The first man to whom Gottlieb apprenticed himself was much impressed by a pair of double-barreled pistols made by the youngster, who chased the barrels and carved the walnut butts with his own exquisite designs. Eager for broader experience, he joined a second master who, fortunately, soon after was appointed Court gunmaker at Stuttgart. There Gottlieb became friendly with several prominent men who influenced his life. He worked by day at a machine factory near Stuttgart and at night studied in the mechanical training college associated with the industrial firm.

In three years he saved enough money to enroll for a two-year engineering course at the Stuttgart Polytechnic, where a fellow student was Max Duttenhofer, who years later became the first chairman of the board of Daimler's motor company.

With the help of a patron from Stuttgart, Daimler went to England and briefly worked with an outstanding mechanical engineering firm; he was similarly employed in Belgium and France before returning to Germany. While foreman at an engineering plant in Reutlingen, he met Wilhelm Maybach, who would in time be Daimler's partner.

Daimler was Technical Director of a Karlsruhe manufacturing business for five years, going abroad several times as representative of the Imperial Government of Württemberg. In 1872 he accepted the position of Technical Director of the company headed by Nikolaus A. Otto, the co-inventor of the internal combustion engine and the four-stroke Otto cycle. Daimler was invaluable to the firm because of his association with engineering experts, German and foreign, many of whom visited the gas-engine factory near Cologne. The chief engineer was Wilhelm Maybach, taken on at Daimler's suggestion. Disapproving of Otto's disinterest in making internal combustion engines suitable for powering vehicles, Daimler left the company in 1881.

Returning from an inspection of oil industry operations in Russia, he set up an experimental workshop at Cannstatt and persuaded Maybach to join him. Their first engine, consisting of a horizontal, air-cooled, single cylinder and a large cast-iron flywheel, was the first speed engine of its kind, capable of 900 r.p.m. In November, 1883, they built their second engine, with crankshaft enclosed, for the first motorcycle.

The motorcycle engine was unique because of its tube ignition, patented by Daimler. The self-timed ignition was made of a hollow plastic tube attached to the cylinder in the position of the spark plug. The outer portion of the tube was heated by a Bunsen burner, causing the charge in the tube to ignite. Independent of the rest of the mechanism, the ignition had the advantage of being lightweight with high-speed potential; the disadvantage was the open flame of the burner.

The one-half horsepower engine had two speeds, with power conveyed by two belts. An exhaust box lessened the sound of the motor. The driver regulated the fuel by a tap gadget and started the cycle by connecting the engine to the rear wheel by a lever, bolt and jockey pulley system. When a control lever was pulled back, the motorcycle was stopped by a cord-operated brake.

In the fall of 1886, Daimler patented a motorboat, previously put through several test runs. He had difficulty getting people to board his boat because they understandably feared that the machinery might blow up. Persuasion failing, the designer turned to subterfuge, connecting insulated wires to dummy control knobs. Thereafter he encountered no resistance from prospective passengers deceived into thinking the motorboat was electrically powered.

Daimler and Maybach, well pleased with their engine designs, were not wholly satisfied with the performances of either their motorcycle or their motorboat. They were more optimistic about a motor vehicle patented on October 9, 1886.

Unlike Benz, Daimler spent no time worrying about the frame of his automobile. He envisioned the conversion of every horse-drawn vehicle to power and, for the body of his first automobile model, chose a carriage with its shafts removed.

The single engine of about one and a half horsepower was placed between the front seat and the back. In the absence of steering pivots, the steering gear moved the front axle and spring. Two speeds were passed to the rear wheels by a friction clutch; and two gearwheels, taking the drive from the engine, moved on their shaft. There was no differential gear, the turning action being effected by leather disks. Air cooling was provided by a fan under the cylinder. In its first trial run, Daimler's automobile reached a speed of eighteen kilometers per hour.

While tests of the automobile continued, Daimler experimented in other fields. He designed a trolley car and built a narrow-gauge track for it; provided a four-power engine for the first navigable balloon, which was launched on September 1, 1887; and, the following year, showed a fire-extinguishing pump, driven by a Daimler engine, at an exhibition of fire-fighting equipment.

Having moved from the workshop, too small for extensive operations, Daimler and Maybach scrapped the frame and engine of their first automobile. Their second car resembled the first only in number of wheels: four. Its engine, vertically placed at the rear, was cooled by water circulating through the tubular frame. Gearwheels, making four speeds possible, transmitted the power to the rear wheels. Their third automobile, belt-driven, had a V-engine of two cylinders, a differential gear, and a jet or surface carburetor. That model was patented in 1889.

Daimler continued to design engines for motorboats, craft for pleasure and commerce. In May, 1889, Otto von Bismarck bought a small Daimler boat with a one-horsepower, single-cylinder engine. Single-cylinder and twin-cylinder Daimler engines powered boats then being used in place of lighters for transferring cargo from warehouses to ships in the harbor of Hamburg. Afterward, authorities ordered larger boats with four-horsepower Daimler engines capable of 12 k.p.h.

Daimler was as progressive in his business dealings as in his engineering experimentation. Certain early patents, granted by Daimler to a Belgian named Sarazin, were given to Emile Levassor of Paris when that manufacturer married the widow of Sarazin. The firm of Panhard and Levassor, already well established as manufacturers of many kinds of machines, was a leading force of the automobile industry in France.

In November, 1890, Daimler Motoren Gesellschaft was founded with Max Duttenhofer as chairman and Daimler vice-chairman. A year later, Daimler and Maybach returned to experimental design, not actively to rejoin the manufacturing company until 1895. Patents for Daimler motors in Great Britain, Ireland, and all the colonies but Canada were held by Frederick Simms, a longtime friend of Daimler's. The Daimler Motor Syndicate formed by Simms was bought by a man named Lawson, and the company became Daimler Motor Company, Ltd.

Emile Jellinek, a Viennese tycoon and an investor in Panhard and Levassor, was much impressed by the race performance of a car with a Daimler engine. That automobile covered a run from Paris to Rouen and return at a speed of over twenty kilometers per hour. Jellinek, who knew Daimler, went to Cannstatt to discuss the possibility of a lighter and more powerful automobile. He also asked for dealership of such cars in France, where he was Austro-Hungarian Consul at Nice. An agreement was made, and Jellinek became a director of the Daimler firm in April, 1900, less than a month after the death of Daimler.

Jellinek suggested that sales in France might be higher if Daimler cars were called something else, not German, and the parent firm approved Mercédès, the name of Jellinek's daughter. Because of German economic conditions in 1926, the Benz and Daimler firms were merged and became the company known as Mercédès-Benz.

AND AFTER

The name commonly identified with the early American automobile is that of Henry Ford, the farsighted inventor who projected and realized his plans for mass production. Less well known are the Duryea brothers, bicycle-makers of Springfield, Massachusetts, who designed and built the first American gasoline-driven automobile in 1892. Construction was begun by Charles E. Duryea (1862–1938) and J. Frank Duryea (1870–1967). In September, 1892, Frank Duryea, working by himself, completed the machine. Whether it was tested that year or not until early in 1893 probably will never be determined because of conflicting claims by the brothers.

Newspaper reports confirm that Frank Duryea drove an automobile in Springfield in 1893. The chassis was a phaeton carriage remodeled only to the extent of strengthening the frame to support a two-cycle engine with hot tube ignition. Power was transmitted by a belt and chain, and steering was done by tiller.

The second Duryea automobile, driven by a clutch and gear, had a heavier flywheel, an improved ignition system and a spray carburetor invented by Charles Duryea. The car, capable of a speed of 10 m.p.h., was kept at 7 m.p.h. during the 1894 test. Its engine weighed 225 pounds, but the brothers planned to lighten their next one to a weight of 175 pounds for propelling a buggy-style chassis.

The 1894 Duryea model is at the Smithsonian Institution in Washington, D.C. A display card describes it as having a "1-cylinder, 4 stroke, 4 horsepower, water-cooled gasoline engine with make-and-break electric ignition. Up-and-down movement of steering tiller for gear shift. Weight 750 pounds."

The brothers established the first American company for the manufacture and sale of automobiles: the Duryea Motor Wagon Company. And Frank Duryea won the first automobile race held in the United States. The race, promoted by the *Times-Herald* in Chicago, was held in that city during a snowstorm on Thanksgiving Day, 1895. Accounts of the race, won by the Duryea Motor Road Wagon, give the average speed as 5 m.p.h. over the more than fifty-mile route. After a subsequent merger, the company started by the two brothers produced Stevens-Duryea automobiles.

Dozens of firms established in the United States after the turn of the century manufactured horseless carriages, most of them with names now chiefly historic. The number of companies decreased as the American demand for practical, mass-produced automobiles increased to more than 97,000,-000 by January 1, 1968, a record destined to fall with each successive year of motor transportation.

Printing was revolutionized in 1886 by the linotype, which may be a curio of historic interest by its centennial.

OTTMAR MERGENTHALER
1854–1899, German-American

In the history of invention, there is no man to whom attribution is more clear-cut than Ottmar Mergenthaler, undisputed inventor of the linotype. That mechanical typesetter, put into operation in the late nineteenth century, revolutionized newspaper printing and book publishing nearly four hundred years after the European manual printing press was invented in Germany by Johann Gutenberg.

Mergenthaler immigrated to the United States from Bietigheim, a small town near Stuttgart where he was a clock and watch maker, not a printer. Born on May 10, 1854, at Hachtel, Germany, Ottmar was one of the five children of Rosine and Johann Georg Mergenthaler. Since Rosine's family had a long history in the teaching guild and Johann was a schoolteacher, it was logical that, like his two older brothers, Ottmar should enter that profession. But Ottmar, to the disappointment of his father, was not interested in teaching.

Dexterous and mechanical by nature, he wanted most of

all to be an engineer, which was an impossibility because of the high tuitions of all good technical institutes. At home Ottmar was adept with tools, keeping domestic machines in repair and, for pleasure, carving wood. He was recognized by neighbors as a dependable repairer of timepieces, from watches to tower clocks. As a career compromise, willingly accepted by Ottmar, he was apprenticed for a nominal fee to a family connection, Louis Hahl, a watchmaker of Bietigheim.

Quick to learn and easy to get along with, the fourteen-year-old Ottmar was popular in Hahl's little workshop, and twelve months before the completion of his four-year apprenticeship, he was put on salary. Accustomed to hard work at home, where his chores made life "all work and no play," as he later wrote, the youngster filled his evenings at Bietigheim with classes in mechanical drawing and other trade-related subjects.

Job opportunities were scarce in Germany in 1872, the year that Ottmar finished his training. The end of the Franco-Prussian War had increased the number of available workers while lessening the number of jobs dependent on war contracts. Like many other disaffected German youths reluctant to do their required military service, Mergenthaler decided to leave the country. More fortunate than most young men, he had the promise of a job in the United States from August Hahl, son of the master under whom Ottmar served his apprenticeship.

August Hahl, an instrument-maker with a workshop in Washington, D.C., advanced passage money to Mergenthaler, whose ship landed at Baltimore, Maryland. In that city, not long after, he was to invent his linotype and, years later, was to have his name perpetuated by a trade school that still exists.

Mergenthaler could not have chosen by specification a better place for employment than the busy workshop in Washington. Hahl, with a staff of skilled workmen, made bells, clocks, precision instruments and models for the designs of American and foreign inventors. The invention model was required for every application to the United States Patent Office.

Although Mergenthaler's knowledge of electricity was limited to an elementary course in theory taken at Bietigheim, he quickly learned to use electric tools. Already expert at clockmaking, he easily mastered the transition from that craft to the fashioning of weather instruments for the United States Signal Service: heliographs and devices for measuring wind velocity and natural precipitation, both rain and snow. He often consulted with inventors, advising them about improvements of their models under construction at the shop.

For business reasons, following the financial panic of 1873, Hahl decided to move his workshop to Baltimore, against the advice of Mergenthaler. The young German, by then shop foreman and, in Hahl's absences, business manager, saw the disadvantage of being thirty-eight miles away from the patent center that attracted inventors; realistically, he knew that the depression was also affecting Baltimore trade. Hahl moved his shop to Baltimore in the late summer of 1874 and barely managed to keep it going for the next two years.

In August, 1876, Charles Moore, an inventor from West Virginia, arrived at the Hahl workshop with a model of what he called a writing machine. Moore's financial backers, including James O. Clephane, the adviser of C. L. Sholes, inventor of the typewriter, were unwilling to put up more capital unless the writing machine could be made to work.

Moore claimed that poor workmanship by a contract machine shop was the reason for the faulty operation of his writing machine. It was designed to reproduce print, obviating typesetting by hand, which was expensive, and making possible multiple duplication by lithographic process. Mergenthaler, inspecting Moore's invention, found the design itself to be inadequate, and suggested remodeling the machine with simplifications.

Mergenthaler, like Moore and his backers, was well aware of the need for a mechanical typesetter. Typesetting had advanced hardly at all from the eleventh century when Pi Sheng, a Chinese printer, invented movable type of clay characters, an invention unknown to Gutenberg, whose movable type was made of metal. On the other hand, by 1876 printing was a relatively rapid process, steam-powered rotary presses having been in operation for a decade, but typesetting was still a slow manual process.

A pressroom compositor of columns for newspapers and pages for books worked with individual metal slugs, representing letters and standard type characters, fitted into wooden trays. Sentences were formed in a composing stick and then transferred a few lines at a time to a metal tray called a galley. When the particular piece of copy, transferred into print, was run off, the printer had to replace each piece of type into the tray from which he had so short a time before picked it out—by hand. The margin for error and the cost of labor were both high.

Moore's machine was an attempt to by-pass typesetting by manipulating lettered keys. The characters, set on a type wheel, were printed on a paper strip afterward cut to fit the length of the line designated. The strip was placed on a lithographic stone for printing.

Mergenthaler's remodeled machine seemed to be an improvement on Moore's: A shift key, like that of a typewriter, changed the letters from Roman to italics. Printing was rapid and the print, sharp. Justification, the spacing of letters to produce the exact line length, was accurate.

Lithographing from the paper strip, however, was far from satisfactory. The stone failed to take every impression. Certain kinds of paper became irreparably smudged by oil from the machine and from the hands of the operator. Too much ink, or too little, affected the production. There were just too many variables in lithographing for the writing machine to be practical.

Clephane, unwilling to give up the project for which he had high hopes, proposed that Mergenthaler should convert the writing machine for use in stereotype instead of lithography. The stereotype, invented in the early eighteenth century, is a printing plate of type metal made from a mold of paper pulp or, less commonly, plaster of Paris. Stereotype, supplanted by the more durable electrotype for book publishing, excelled as a technique in the printing of periodicals, the giant cylinder presses of newspapers being fitted with curved stereotype plates.

The paper pulp substance chosen by Mergenthaler for the

stereotype writing machine was papier-mâché, made with the addition of glue, rosin and clay. He had his reservations about the practicality of making impressions of the machine's letters and other characters directly on the papier-mâché, but Clephane would not be put off.

As Mergenthaler expected, it was difficult to make uniform impressions on the papier-mâché, but by the late fall of 1878, the typeface was ready for testing. The letters on papier-mâché, cut into ribbons or strips, were fairly well defined, and the justification was satisfactory. Independent lines of the ribbon type were placed in a mold designed for simultaneous casting of forty lines.

In operation the machine was a disaster. Liquid type-metal chilled too rapidly for even distribution in the mold that was set in a casting box. Heating the mold to the temperature of the liquid type-metal was equally ineffective because the type-metal penetrated every part of the mold and ruined the matrix, making it difficult to remove the letter slugs. During printing the papier-mâché was supposed to be soft, but keeping it at the correct degree of wetness was one more difficult problem for Mergenthaler to solve. Every so often good castings were made, but the hit-or-miss system was not commercially sound. Pulled proofs showed conclusively that the papier-mâché matrix was undependable; letters were distorted and their depth varied, dependent on their size and shape.

Mergenthaler knew he was wasting his time on a machine that would never work, and Hahl agreed. After working on the stereotype model through the summer of 1879, Mergenthaler flatly refused to continue any longer. The machine and tools were moved to Washington where inventors on the staff of the company of Clephane and his associates worked for several more years before abandoning the project.

In 1879, Mergenthaler had the inspiration for a line-by-line composing machine as opposed to the letter-by-letter method. In a matter of hours he drew plans for a machine with parallel bands, containing fixed type that was to be raised or lowered to form a word-line. A matrix of the line was to be made by pressing a papier-mâché strip against the type. Mergenthaler was later to regret that he ripped the band-machine drawings into shreds during a fit of despondency over a financial crisis in Hahl's business.

When August Hahl was given a period of grace by his bank, he set out to solicit new business while Mergenthaler stayed at the shop to fill orders that steadily increased. Made a full partner by Hahl on January 1, 1881, Mergenthaler was married in September of that same year to Miss Emma Lachenmayer, whose father was a Baltimore architect.

At the invitation of Clephane, Mergenthaler went to Washington for a discussion about the stereotype machine still being revised, but he refused to take an offered consultancy. In the course of conversation with Clephane and his associates, Mergenthaler casually mentioned his band machine idea, sketching a rough of the plans he had thrown into a wastebasket.

With the encouragement of his wife, Mergenthaler spent much of his leisure time on the design of his band machine, making blueprints instead of drawings. The firm of Hahl and Mergenthaler being solvent and prosperous, he was under no pressure to rush through the design of his machine. Its plans were unfinished when Clephane arrived in Baltimore bubbling with the news that he had presented the idea of the band machine to an interested backer, Lemon G. Hine.

Hine, a Washington lawyer and a commissioner of that city, was a man of integrity and vision. He saw the merit of Mergenthaler's machine at their first meeting and agreed to raise capital for the project. On being informed not long after that the funds were available, Mergenthaler resigned from Hahl's firm and set up in business for himself on January 1, 1883.

Mergenthaler's first band model, small, experimental and crude though it was, clearly demonstrated that the design principle had merit. A working scale model, successfully tested in the fall of 1883, presented one major operational fault: The machine worked too fast for the matrix to dry on the type. Stripping off the matrix while it was still wet was inefficient and time-consuming. The use of metal for the matrix material was beyond Mergenthaler's means; the machine contained 4,500 types and these, in steel, would cost two dollars each.

Faced with prohibitive production costs for a machine fitted with metal matrices, Mergenthaler came up with a brilliant idea for an alternative: one machine for casting and composing. He built a model with characters at the edges of narrow brass bands, their thickness tapered from top to bottom. By keyboard manipulation the bands were successively dropped to the level desired, and then molten metal from a casting mechanism was forced through a mold to produce a slug.

The first of the combination band machines was tested in July, 1884, with Mergenthaler composing a line on the keyboard and hand-turning the driving pulley. Steam power was then attached, another line composed, and the stopper removed from the metal pump. The matrices were dropped down, clamped into place and aligned. Molten type-metal was discharged by the pump, and a finished slug of a perfect printing-surface line dropped from the machine. The entire procedure took fifteen seconds, including the return of the matrix bands to their normal position.

The backers were jubilant over the test, but Mergenthaler recognized its shortcomings: It lacked a justification system, spacing being done by the machine operator. The matrix bands were not true. And, unable to see errors made while tapping key after key, the operator had to throw out lines that contained mistakes.

Again Mergenthaler, ever creative, had new ideas for the improvement of his machine. The master plan was for a single-matrix machine in which an individual matrix could be automatically dropped to position by the tap of a key. The backers, with a great show of confidence in the perfectionist inventor, agreed to delay production of the band machine and waited while Mergenthaler labored for months over revisions of the single-matrix machine.

The simplest improvement was the justifying of each line by the use of graduated wedge spacers to be placed between the words. The individual matrix, stored with others in vertical copper tubes, dropped at the touch of a key to a tiny track, from which it was blown to its line position by air. The operator, able to see the matrix, could immediately make a necessary correction; at will, he inserted italics and any unusual characters. The most difficult task was in producing inexpensive matrices of high quality. Failing to get a strong and sharp matrix from outside contractors, Mergenthaler set up a separate workshop for matrix manufacture. It required thirty special machines and many miscellaneous attachments to make matrices at a cost low enough to keep the line-by-line machine at a reasonable price.

By the time the machine was ready for a test in the summer of 1885, a controlling interest in the original company had been bought for $300,000 by a syndicate. The syndicate membership included newspapermen from Louisville, Chicago, Washington and New York. Whitelaw Reid, of the *New York Tribune,* was president and general manager of the newly organized Mergenthaler Printing Company. One of the first machines was installed in the composing room of the *New York Tribune* in July, 1886. For a group of printers and reporters, the thirty-two-year-old Mergenthaler demonstrated the single line of type produced by the steam-powered machine operated by a keyboard. When asked the name of the machine, Whitelaw Reid told reporters that it would be known as the *linotype.*

From the first, Mergenthaler had difficulties with the officers of the company that bore his name. They wanted immediate production of one hundred machines, although there existed no organization or factory space for the manufacture of such a number. After unavailing argument for a first order of only twelve, Mergenthaler set about to comply with the demands of the new financial backers. He obtained adequate factory space, designed new tools for making specialized parts, and instructed machinists inexperienced in the assembling of the machines and in subsequent servicing.

Efficiency of operation was achieved in spite of the delivery delays by contractors and the scarcity of trained workmen. More than fifty machines were delivered by February, 1888; the schedule of production was projected for delivery of the remainder by March and the completion of an order of a second hundred by July.

Dubious transactions, discrediting the syndicate and the officers of the company, resulted in the resignation of Mergenthaler as factory manager in the late spring of 1888. Reid at once ordered the removal of the factory of the Mergenthaler Printing Company from Baltimore and its relocation in Brooklyn, New York. Mergenthaler, disheartened, sold a considerable number of his own shares of stock in order to set up a new machine shop.

It seemed for a short time that Mergenthaler's case might be parallel to that of Gutenberg. The German printer whose most outstanding work was the Mazarin Bible, historically known as the Gutenberg Bible, lost his invention to a creditor. Unable to repay a loan, Gutenberg forfeited his prized types and his printing press to Johann Fust, a goldsmith. With a partner, Fust established a successful printing business in which Gutenberg had no equity.

Mergenthaler sued to recover his own tools, taken to Brooklyn along with the total contents of his factory; but he was never fully compensated for that loss or for others resulting from the syndicate's tactics, which were, to understate the facts, high-handed.

Established at a new business site, Mergenthaler turned his full attention to the linotype, with which he was far from satisfied. In composing-room operation, the machine proved to have some annoying drawbacks and certain serious faults.

The inventor redesigned the machine on paper with the cooperation of an expert draftsman, and personally supervised mechanical corrections. He remade the keyboard touch, making it invariably uniform and less hard, correcting the conditions that had occasionally caused matrices to fly out of their channels, or tracks. Reliability of locking-up and alignment was increased, the distributor was strengthened, and the whole machine opened up for accessibility to a machinist making repairs. The air blast of the blower lino-type was done away with, in part because the noise distracted operators. Matrices, instead of being positioned by the air blast, dropped by gravity from magazines placed on the diagonal to the line position. At the conclusion of the casting process, an arm, replacement of the distributing elevator, raised the matrices to the top of the machine from where they automatically dropped into storage boxes.

Major changes and minor adjustments were incorporated in meticulously drawn sketches for Mergenthaler's last and most efficient machine, which he called the *Simplex Linotype*. Money for the model was raised by Clephane, who was distressed by the syndicate management's treatment of Mergenthaler. The Simplex, first demonstrated in New York, in 1890, was an immediate success, being stronger and faster than the blower type. Orders for machines, leased or purchased outright, poured in from the United States, Canada, and even England.

The Washington stockholders, old and true friends of Mergenthaler, took control of the company, reorganizing it, in 1891, as the Mergenthaler Linotype Company. The company started a training program for linotypers, and established good relationship with unions of typographers who were assured of more jobs because of the increase of printing resulting from the installations of linotypes.

Mergenthaler had about a year to enjoy the results of his long labor over the machine that revolutionized the printing business, decreasing production costs, increasing the number of pages of daily papers and the number of books published. After a triumphal 1892 European tour highlighted by heart-warming reunions in Germany, Mergenthaler developed tuberculosis. Following a severe attack of pleurisy in 1888, he had been warned to eat sensibly, sleep regularly, and work less strenuously. He disregarded both the medical advice and the recurrent spells of weakness that were fore-runners of the disease he never shook off. For his health, he left Baltimore in 1894, staying successively in the Blue Ridge Mountains of Virginia; at Saranac Lake, New York; in Prescott, Arizona; and Deming, New Mexico. An invalid, for the most part bedridden, he returned to Maryland in 1898, and the following year, at the age of forty-five, died in his Baltimore home.

AND AFTER

Mergenthaler had no idea that he was being prophetic when, at a Washington banquet honoring him, he said, "I am convinced, gentlemen, that unless some method of printing can be designed which requires no type at all, the method embodied in our invention will be the one used in the future; not alone because it is cheaper, but mainly because it is destined to secure superior quality."

"No type at all" is used by computers already operating in printing businesses of various kinds. And what is brand-new today is expected to be passé tomorrow.

Setting type by photographic means is speeding the production of printing. Small electronic systems and huge computer assemblages are available for the newspaper business. For the daily paper of only a few pages, there is a computer which makes copy corrections, turns out the required size and face of the type, justifying to the specified line width. The news story, tapped out on an electric typewriter, is recorded on paper and magnetic tape. Copy corrections are made on a second tape which, along with the first, is placed in a computer. The corrected copy, turned out at 150 words a minute, is photographed for the press run.

Cathode-ray-tube typesetters produce 120 newspaper lines a minute and do other printing jobs even faster. Highly sophisticated computers, not yet economically feasible for newspaper printing, set many thousands of characters a second; one, not restricted to the line-by-line system, page-prints up to 10,000 a second. Certain kinds of books are being "typewritten" by a machine that turns out justified copy.

It is accepted as fact that the photocomposition dependent on cameras will be outmoded well before the turn of the next century. Laser projectors will transmit pictures and copy from the computer to electrostatic presses. Printing reproduction processes of today, like silk screen and xerography, will within the foreseeable future be replaced by techniques being perfected or dreamed of in the creative minds of twentieth-century inventors.

An American who applied for more than a thousand patents made major inventions based on sound, light and motion.

THOMAS ALVA EDISON
1847–1931, American

Pictures in motion were the subjects of experimentation centuries before the birth of Thomas Alva Edison and, even without him, the ultimate development of motion pictures was inevitable. But it was consistent with Edison's far-ranging interests that the impetus for the popular commercial movie should have come from his laboratory. What seems surprising is that the inventor of the phonograph and the incandescent light bulb neither successfully linked sound and film nor artificially lighted movie sets. Both klieg lights for illuminating indoor sets and the sound track on film followed, by several decades, the demonstration of the Edison laboratory's peep-show device called the Kinetoscope.

Edison, more than a great inventor, was motivated to improve consumer services and to design products certain to gain customer acceptance. His practicality was apparent from business ventures undertaken when he was an enterprising youth, living in Port Huron, Michigan. At twelve, he set up street stalls where teen-agers in his employ sold newspapers, vegetables and fruits. Edison, as a butcher boy on a train from Port Huron to Detroit, worked a fourteen-hour day; after his return from the round-trip run, he then hawked newspapers from ten until midnight. To rail travelers he sold sweets and periodicals, and later was to invent waxed paper for packaging candy and cookies. He bought produce for his Port Huron stalls in Detroit and transported his stock aboard the train he worked, without being asked to pay freight charges. In time he dropped the produce business and concentrated on more profitable wares: periodicals and newspapers. For a while he published his own newspaper, *The Weekly Herald*, setting the type in an unused train compartment. In the same small space he did experiments with chemicals that he purchased with profits from his various undertakings.

Through association with telegraphers along the railroad line, Edison became interested in telegraphing news and learned to be an operator. At fifteen, he was employed at a telegraph office and, at sixteen, designed an automatic system for setting off the routine hourly time-signals of night operators. After losing his job for negligence, he spent five years as an itinerant telegraph operator.

In 1868, Edison, experienced and competent, went to work in the Western Union office at Boston, Massachusetts. Soon after, he took out his first patent. It was for an electrical vote recorder with which members of Congress could vote from their seats on the floor of the Senate or the House. The voting device was pooh-poohed at his demonstration, the elected officials turning it down with derision. His second patent, for a stock ticker, was not profitable because of the limited number of potential customers in Boston. At twenty-two, Edison decided to move to New York and arrived there almost penniless, without prospect of a job.

Within months he had a good position, offered after he rapidly and skillfully repaired the overloaded ticker system of the Gold Indicator Company. Shortly he started, with F. L. Pope, the firm of Pope, Edison & Company for the purpose of designing and operating telegraphic equipment. The partners, calling themselves electrical engineers, pioneered the profession of electrical engineering that was to boom in the following seventy-five years. They designed a stock ticker to operate on one wire, an apparatus that Edison improved at the request of the president of the Gold & Stock Telegraph Company. Patented improvements included a *unison stop* for setting all tickers at zero from a central transmitter.

With the $40,000 he received for ticker inventions, Edison set up a plant for the manufacture of tickers, his chief customer being the Gold & Stock Telegraph Company. He was twenty-three years old and the employer of fifty factory workers. It was an incredible achievement for a young man who had been labeled a dull-witted child in his native town, Milan, Ohio. Thomas Edison, born February 11, 1847, had only a few months of formal schooling and rather haphazard tutoring from his mother, who had been a schoolteacher. He was handicapped by early deafness, whether congenital or accidental is not certain, but the assumption of his elders that Thomas was mentally retarded was obviously erroneous.

At Edison's New York factory and at his laboratory established in 1876 at Menlo Park, twenty-five miles outside the city, he employed topflight experts, as he did ever after. A number of men with mechanical skills made their first inventive contributions while working with Edison, and then branched out, establishing their own companies.

During the time Edison patented forty-six devices for stock tickers, he was also engaged in concentrated research on an electric telegraph system. His electromagnetic shunt with soft iron core for use in high-speed telegraphy was an important contribution to land transmission. One of his most notable inventions was the quadruplex telegraphy of 1874. It was an apparatus for the simultaneous sending of two messages in one direction and two in the opposite, over one wire.

His carbon transmitter for the telephone invented by Alexander Graham Bell was a practical improvement for which Edison received $6,000 a year for seventeen years. He received a similar amount of money for the same time period for his telephone relay, in which a lever at the end of a wire was triggered by moistened chalk; current made the chalk slippery, and the lever, slipping, was automatically activated. Previously the lever had been magnetically operated. For both the transmitter and the relay, Edison chose the annual payment instead of a lump sum because he was aware of his predilection for putting available resources into experimentation and research projects.

When Edison was an itinerant operator, he designed a telegraphic instrument on a principle that was the basis for his invention of the phonograph, 1877. He had worked out a telegraphic device for the rapid recording of press reports to be played back at a later time. The reports were recorded by indentations on a disk of paper which was the playback, or repeater, that the receiving operator could "read" slowly whenever he chose.

The lever of Edison's telegraphic device gave off a musical note when the paper disk was operating at high speed, and that phenomenon stayed in the inventor's mind. His very first experiment with recording the human voice on a similar instrument worked on its initial test. The record of his phonograph was a horizontal cylinder covered with tin foil, regularly grooved in lateral direction and irregularly grooved in depth, a system afterward referred to as hill-and-dale. For recording, there was a needle set in a diaphragm above the cylinder which was slowly rotated. Edison made the first recording attempt, speaking loudly the words "Mary had a little lamb." His voice vibrated the diaphragm, moving the needle which made indentations in the tin foil on the cylinder. On playback the words were distinct and clear.

In spite of the low-cost construction of the instrument, only eighteen dollars, Edison did nothing about commercializing it for a decade. Then, working through five days and five nights, he made the necessary practical adjustments. However, when he patented his phonograph in 1878, he made a list of its potentials, projecting into another century and to present-day phonograph records of music and the spoken word. He forecast dictation; talking books for the blind; telephone connections for message-taking and the preservation of conversations; family voice-albums, even for the final words of the dying; clock systems with verbal instructions for schedule-keeping; talking toys; and of course music reproduction, instrumental and vocal.

Development of the phonograph was in part delayed by Edison's preoccupation with electricity. In 1878, he began to experiment with electric light bulbs, or lamps. Initial work on the carbon lamp had been done in England, but Edison produced the first commercial incandescent light bulb. He discarded hundreds of substances containing carbon before deciding on bamboo fibers as superior for his filament, and investigated economical processes of manufacturing glass for reasonably priced bulbs.

Edison and his assistants at Menlo Park studied every aspect of electrical power and electrical systems. His laboratory did research on vacuum techniques, wiring materials, fuses, sockets, storage batteries, motors, conductors and generators. Edison designed workable large dynamos with low internal resistance, proving wrong those experts who thought fusing would result from strong current supplied by a central station.

The world's first light and power plant was built by Edison in New York City; with that Pearl Street plant, completed in 1882, he established electrical distribution as a commercial product. The economy of the country was improved by the setting up of electricity supply stations of the Edison company, which gave employment to many engineers, and of factories for manufacturing electrical equipment in great demand by consumers.

The *Edison effect* was a scientific result incidental to experiments with the incandescent bulb. Edison, observing the slow blackening of glass bulbs in use, tried to find out why the gradual deposit was less where the filament plane cut across the bulb. He interpreted that to indicate that one part of the filament protected the bulb from carbon atoms from the other part. It was not Edison who carried the study to its conclusion, which was that blackening came from electrons emitted from the heated filament. That investigation led to the invention of the vacuum tube and to radio communication.

Edison made his first sketchy notes on a motion-picture camera in 1887, the same year that he opened his laboratory at West Orange, New Jersey. Like his original laboratory at Menlo Park, the second was an industrial research center where teams of experts were assigned to specific projects. The key man of the motion-picture experiments was William Kennedy Laurie Dickson, a photographer on the staff.

Dickson and Edison were familiar with the motion-picture experiments of their contemporaries on both sides of the Atlantic Ocean and with historical attempts to present pictures in motion. A projection instrument, *Magia Catoptrica,* was invented by an outstanding scientist of the seventeenth century, Athanasius Kircher, a German Jesuit priest. In 1645, Kircher demonstrated his invention in Rome, projecting hand-drawn still transparencies on a viewing surface, a technique similar to that of modern slides thrown on a projection screen.

The possibility of showing still images in rapid movement fascinated Peter Mark Roget, a British physician and long-time secretary of the Royal Society. The indefatigable Roget not only actively practiced medicine but, meantime, spent fifty years compiling his *Thesaurus of English Words and Phrases,* a work carried on by his heirs. In the 1820's Roget experimented with pictures in motion and presented a paper

on the subject to the Royal Society, elaborating on the fact
that the image of a moving object is retained by the eye for a
second after the motion is observed. While looking at a moving object through a Venetian blind, Roget was struck by the
idea that motion, broken into a series of separate phases,
might be simulated. To illustrate his theory, he rapidly
turned pages on which photographs were mounted, and revolved wheels and disks circled with pictures.

Similar demonstrations of pictures placed on rotating devices were given by several Europeans at about the same
time. In Austria, a projection machine for viewing pictures
in simulated motion was marketed in 1853. By the early
1870's, several reports of studies of animal locomotion were
in print. Those led to photographs of a horse in motion
taken in the United States by Eadweard Muybridge (1830–
1904), an Englishman.

Muybridge's experiments, subsidized by Leland Stanford,
railroad tycoon, politician and founder of Stanford University, were conducted at Stanford's stud farm in Palo Alto,
California. The first pictures were taken in June, 1878, with
twelve small cameras set twenty-one inches apart along a
fence beside a running-track. The track surface was covered
with corrugated rubber to prevent rising dust from obscur-
ing the camera image. Electrically operated shutters of the
cameras were closed by circuit-breaking. When a trotting
horse and sulky were photographed, the camera shutters
were triggered by wire laid on the track so a single wheel of
the vehicle passed over each; by a horse, with or without
rider, the cameras were activated by the breaking of strings
stretched across the track. In 1879, the number of cameras
was increased to twenty-four, and the space between then

was decreased; two other cameras were respectively placed at the starting line and at the far end of the stretch.

The photographs of the Stanford horses in motion lacked fine detail, the exposure time being very short, but the prints were widely exhibited. In 1881, Muybridge finished his projecting device, the zoopraxiscope, which was an adaptation of two earlier inventions for demonstrating the persistence of vision. The following year, he began a long series of studies of animal motion, human and four-footed, for the University of Pennsylvania.

Muybridge lectured in West Orange in the late winter of 1888, and two days later visited Edison at his laboratory. There is controversy among historians about whether the inventor of the phonograph and the photographer of objects that could be shown in motion discussed combining sound and pictures. In his *Animals in Motion,* published in 1899, Muybridge wrote that on February 27, 1888, he discussed with Edison the "practicability" of using the zoopraxiscope in conjunction with the phonograph.

On October 8, 1888, Edison wrote his first motion-picture caveat, a description of an invention to be filed at the patent office, pending execution of the object. All of Edison's several-motion-picture caveats were generalizations, none containing specifics of the cameras or the viewing devices. The original declaration of intent began, "I am experimenting upon an instrument which does for the Eye what the phonograph does for the Ear . . ."

After the filing of the caveat, Dickson attempted to adapt the phonograph technique to an instrument for the eye. Again a rotated cylinder was the recording surface; it was, however, coated with photographic emulsion, not covered with tin foil like the first phonograph model. A tiny camera replaced the phonograph's diaphragm and needle above the cylinder. The need to intermittently stop the camera for registering the picture on the emulsion presented a major technical problem.

Long and discouraging experimentation by Edison and Dickson at last resulted in a camera that could be stopped and started forty-eight times a second. The pictures, not even as big as pinheads, spiraled the cylinder like the sound waves of the phonograph. The two inventors were fully aware of the limitations of their microphotographic device for producing moving pictures; the chief disadvantage was the inability to play back the machine.

The search for another recording medium for pictures in motion ended when Edison purchased a length of Eastman's flexible photographic film. Edison's kinetograph once more depended on a cylinder. The inventor standardized motion-picture film for the future by regular placement of holes along the edge of the strip of film, and by the arbitrary fixing of the width and size of the strips. High-speed emulsions coated the strong, flexible, celluloid-base material cut in strips, the strip film. It was moved forward by ratchet gear. A demonstration of the kinetograph was given in the fall of 1889.

Revisions of the camera continued at the laboratory where a stock-band viewing device, the Kinetoscope, was developed. The Kinetoscope was a peep-show instrument, permitting only one person at a time to look at the flickering image on the film run off by an arrangement set inside. The first public showing was to convention members of the Women's Club of America at Edison's workshop in the laboratory at West Orange. In a newspaper account of the demonstration, the reporter of the New York *Sun* wrote, on May 28: "The surprised and pleased clubwomen saw a small pine box standing on the floor. There were some wheels and belts near the box, and a workman who had them in charge. In the top of the box was a hole perhaps an inch in diameter. As they looked through this hole they saw the picture of a man. It was most marvelous. It bowed and smiled and waved its hand and took off its hat with the most perfect naturalness and grace. Every motion was perfect. No wonder Edison chuckled with the effect he produced with his Kinetograph."

Actors for Edison's noncommercial films were strictly amateur recruits from the laboratory. It was one of them who went through the motions of waving, bowing and hat-tipping with "naturalness and grace" that fascinated the clubwomen at the workshop showing. Pictures shot in series, designed for simulating motion when shown at high speed, were purchased for experiments; some of the Muybridge photographs were included. Eventually the need for entertaining features necessitated the filming by Edison's own staff of attention-holding subjects, primarily of physical contests and activities.

In 1889, a small shack covered with tar paper was added to the complex of seven buildings at Edison's laboratory site. The shanty, nicknamed the Black Maria, housed two darkrooms and a photographic studio with a small stage on which performers posed. Historically accepted as the first movie studio, the room, under a roof section of sliding glass, could be mechanically rotated. The arrangement was to take advantage of sunshine, natural light for battery-operated cameras set up in front of the stage.

Edison was in Europe when the Black Maria was constructed under the supervision of Dickson, who needed extra space for various expanding photographic experiments. On his return Edison observed filming procedures, but neither then nor later did the inventor of the incandescent bulb try to shoot his movie sequences with the use of footlights, floodlights, spotlights or any other artificial illumination technique.

Various trial-and-error methods for filming preceded the adoption of a strip-feeding mechanism for the movie camera, and both the Kinetograph and the Kinetoscope were constantly under adjustment and revision. Since Edison's phonographs, installed in various public places, proved to be profitable coin-in-the-slot instruments for the entertainment of the curious, he thought the Kinetoscope might have equal attraction.

There was so much widespread anticipation of the much talked about motion pictures that Edison, in 1894, opened the Kinetoscope Parlor in New York. It was the first motion-picture house and, for two years, drew large audiences of people who individually viewed the feature films. By 1896, the Edison Manufacturing Company had built more than nine hundred Kinetoscopes.

Edison publicly mentioned a "device for a telephone, so that you can see the man you are talking to" and, in the privacy of his laboratory, worked toward a picture-with-sound instrument. The machine, the Kinetophone, was designed with the earphones of a phonograph synchronized to

Edison's Kinetoscope; somewhat faulty electric synchronization was achieved in 1912. The Kinetoscope was neither perfect nor practical, there being no way then to amplify sound for an audience. And by that time, even the Kinetoscope was outmoded because of advances in motion-picture production by other inventors and experimenters.

Increasingly in demand as consultant to industry and government, Edison, during World War I, served as president of the U.S. Naval Consulting Board for Inventions. He continued always with electrical developments and experimented with metal refinement processes. He designed an odoroscope for measuring smells and studied sound waves, devising a way to concentrate them along a straight line and inventing an audiophone for the deaf. The major concept and the small device alike interested Edison.

The man who once said, "Invention is one per cent inspiration and ninety-nine per cent perspiration," perspired very little in the last twenty-five years of his life; his hardworking colleagues carried out experiments and perfected techniques derived ninety-nine per cent from Edison's inspiration. Honored for the broad range of his ideas and for his practical accomplishments, Edison died at his home in West Orange on December 18, 1931.

AND AFTER

For the last two decades of the nineteenth century, several experimenters made progress with motion-picture techniques, doing research on the development of a practical celluloid film and constructing ciné-cameras. Prominent in the history of cinematography are the names of William

Friese-Green and Mortimer Evans of England, and Lumière and Marey of France. The Lumière brothers, Louis and Auguste, were astute businessmen who were the first to project their cinephotographs on a screen for a viewing audience. E. J. Marey, a physician more interested in mechanics than medicine, published studies of consecutive movements of animals, which in part were responsible for the subsequent experiments of Muybridge; his photographs, in turn, led Marey to invent devices for showing creatures of nature in motion. Marey designed a photographic gun for maneuverability when taking pictures of birds in flight, and projected the pictures of his *chronophotographe* for scientific purposes.

The first story-line films originated in France, the work of George Méliés, whose specialty was trick photography. Aided by mechanical artifices, he shot his scripts on staged sets, producing his *Cinderella* in 1900 and *A Trip to the Moon* in 1902.

In the United States, the pioneer story-line film was produced by Edwin S. Porter, who gained his experience as a cameraman with the Edison Company. Porter chose an exciting and dramatic subject, true to life, for his *The Great Train Robbery*, 1903. Its continuity was achieved by film editing, one of Porter's several contributions to the improvement of motion-picture techniques. The suspense and thrills of his historic movie influenced other producers, quick to follow his lead.

Color and sound, in that order, were yet to come. An American, Charles Urban, gave a demonstration of color film in England on May 1, 1908; his Kinema color was a two-color process with filters on both the projector and the camera. In the United States, the Prizma was another two-color process done by dyeing the emulsion on both sides of positive prints. In 1915, Dr. Herbert T. Kalmus, a distinguished Boston scientist, started the Technicolor Motion Picture Corporation and introduced color-in-the-film, again limited to two colors. Technicolor's three-color process was not demonstrated in a commercial film until 1933.

Vitaphone, synchronizing a sound disk with film, made possible the first motion picture with its own musical accompaniment: *Don Juan,* 1926. When the disk could be discarded for sound directly in film, talkies became a reality. Several systems were worked out for translating sound waves into electric impulses for the control of light striking a film's sound strip, now known as the sound track. There was partial dialogue on the sound track of *The Jazz Singer,* 1927; and the first all-talking motion picture was *Lights of New York,* 1928.

By 1953, sound recording for motion pictures was commonly made on tracks and tapes of magnetized material. Experimental methods in film-making led to wide screens, spread from wall to wall at the front of the theater and showing actors in gargantuan proportions; to the 3-D method which made it necessary for movie patrons to wear special glasses; and to stereophonic sound effects that encircled the audience. Sound tracks, once limited to 35-mm film for movie houses and to 16-mm for nontheatrical film, finally became available for 8-mm film.

In the early 1960's there was a regression of refined techniques. Producers on tight budgets, who made films of low technical quality and high artistic merit, won awards with inferior technical productions of the type that early experimenters had tried to improve. The future of the motion picture depends on technological advances, some not even in the mind of man, and on existent electronic and optical devices that will in time be made economically practical.

Television was a logical corollary to the inventions of telegraphy, the radio and motion pictures.

JOHN LOGIE BAIRD
1888–1946, Scottish

VLADIMIR KOSMA ZWORYKIN
1889–   , Russian-American

Practical television systems were invented on opposite sides of the Atlantic Ocean by two men whose experience and research techniques were totally different.

John Logie Baird, a Scotsman who lived most of his adult life in England, expended energy, limited by poor health, on unfortunate business schemes before deciding, almost by whim, to try to invent television. The equipment he assembled in "two tiny attic rooms which formed my laboratory" was makeshift and inferior; some was secondhand and some salvaged from junk piles.

In America, television invention was accomplished by Vladimir Kosma Zworykin, a Russian-born citizen of the United States, who had spent years working in the field of electronics. An electrical engineer and physicist, Zworykin, a trained scientist, conducted his television research in two industrial laboratories that made available to him financial resources, sophisticated scientific equipment and expert technical assistants.

Baird and Zworykin both experimented with a transmitting design patented in 1884 by Paul Nipkow, then a student at Berlin University. He based his invention on the fact that the element selenium has variations of electrical resistance dependent on light exposure. When full sun shines on selenium, electric current flows more freely through the element; with less light, the current is weaker. Nipkow reasoned that by incorporating selenium into a scanning device a motion scene might be electrically transmitted.

He worked out a disk backed by a selenium cell that would change electric current according to variations of light. Nipkow's cardboard disk, designed to have small holes spiraled in a line along its edge, when rotated would break the scene into bright and dark values, depending on the amount of light beamed on the selenium. The scanning disk would transmit the voltages, or signals, in sequence; traveling by wire to a receiver, the signals would there be converted by a similar disk back to light values for reconstruction of the scene. Nipkow in theory arrived at a practical method for transmitting a motion scene, but he was unable to perfect his mechanical system. There was then a lack of sophisticated instruments for building such a device as he planned, and he had no way to amplify the weak electric current from selenium, which reacts too slowly for satisfactory transmission.

Various other inventions of the time contributed ultimately to the development of practical television systems. The photoelectric cell was based on the variations of electrical resistance, and a rapidly reacting one was invented in

1905 by Hans Geitel and Julius Elster, two German scientists. Earlier, Professor Ferdinand Braun of Strasbourg University, improving the existent cathode-ray tube, used his own as an oscilloscope, an instrument that shows in visual patterns the changes in electric currents.

Professor Boris Rosing, at the Petrograd Institute of Technology, began experimenting in 1907 with the transmission of pictures, using Nipkow's disk at the point of transmission and Braun's tube at the receiving end. In a similar experiment in England, A. A. Campbell-Swinton placed cathode-ray tubes at the transmission and receiving points. Another step forward that failed to reach conclusion was made by Max Dieckmann of Munich. In 1909, he published an article on a theoretically workable television system dependent on a cathode-ray tube, and he also constructed a small model over which he transmitted silhouettes. Dieckmann observed that the "remaining problems of image-transmission might be solved more easily with the use of wireless telegraphy than by wire telegraphy." It was a perceptive observation.

In 1922, John Logie Baird began his experiments with television, returning to mechanical and electrical interests from which he had been diverted by sundry business ventures.

Born in Scotland in 1888, John was the youngest son of the parish minister at Helensburgh, Dumbartonshire. Although a frail child, he had a forceful personality that attracted a group of youngsters whose project leader he was. They spent their time, not on the playing field and at other outdoor activities, but in mechanical pursuits.

John was about twelve when he and his friends installed an elaborate telephone system for transmitting and receiving in their individual homes. More complicated than the well-known single-line tin-can phone for talking to the boy next door, the Helensburgh system necessitated the stringing of wires for considerable distances over roadways as well as lawns. When a coachman was dragged from his driving seat by a transmission wire broken by strong wind, the private communication system was doomed. The local telephone company, investigating the accident, traced the broken line to the Bairds' attic, and installations were summarily removed from the homes of all the participants.

On his own, John soon after built a water-driven dynamo with which the minister's manse, previously lit by gas, was supplied with electricity. John then formed a camera club and, being fascinated by photography, converted a discarded magic lantern into an enlarger, and rigged up a device for photographing himself while asleep.

At the Royal Technical College in Glasgow, Baird, like Nipkow before him, became interested in selenium. The college authorities would permit no laboratory experiments unless they were part of a student's assignment, but Baird, not to be thwarted, used the family kitchen as his lab. After receiving his diploma, he worked unhappily in Glasgow at a motor company and for the local electric power company.

Suffering from the cold of Glasgow winters, Baird was very often ill and absent from work. In an attempt to keep warm in his rented room, he wrapped his feet in toilet tissue, pulling his socks over it. That led to his first business venture: he was the head of the company and traveling salesman for the Baird Undersock, a paper product. In a year he cleared about sixteen hundred pounds, but then "closed down the Baird Undersock Company" and, lured by the prospect of a warm climate, sailed for the Caribbean.

With a friend he started an ill-fated fruit jam company in the West Indies where he contracted malaria. Returning to London, he tried to eke out some sort of living by marketing several products, including French soap. For his health he went to Hastings, from which seaside town he wrote to a sister for advice. He asked whether she thought he should try to redesign a glass razor, one he invented having painfully slashed him, or to try to invent television. Her advice was to go with the razor; Baird's decision was to attempt the development of a television system.

Low in funds and below par in health, Baird did his first television experiments in a rooming house and later in a small room over a shop in the Queen's Arcade, Hastings. The sites were no more incongruous for the beginnings of a major invention than his tools for the realization of his goal. His sending apparatus was mounted on his washbasin, and his equipment included an army surplus wireless telegraph, a tea chest, lenses purchased at a bicycle shop, a secondhand electric-fan motor, sealing wax, glue, darning needles, flashlight batteries, valves, transformers, string, electric wires, chips and blocks of wood.

With a pair of scissors he cut up a cardboard hatbox and shaped his scanning disk, which had small holes set in two spirals. The disk, backed by a selenium cell, had a darning needle for a spindle and was revolved by bobbins. The pinpoints in the disk permitted light to travel to a crude receiving instrument set on the tea chest, two feet away. The image scanned by the whirling disk was a Maltese cross cut from cardboard. It was a great day for Baird when, in the spring of 1923, he "was able to show the shadow of the little cross transmitted over a few feet!"

By chance, Baird's invention made newspaper headlines when, having touched a live wire, he was found unconscious on the floor. Baird's landlord rebelled against further experiments that might cause a fire in his building, and after some altercation Baird was served with legal papers terminating his rental arrangements. By then, several potential investors had been to see Baird, who decided to go to London to continue his work.

In an attic on Frith Street, Baird made slow progress with his apparatus, transmitting only outlines of shapes drawn on paper. Knowing that his device was far from ready for public exhibition, he nonetheless agreed to accept a much needed fee for demonstrating television several times a day during anniversary celebrations at Selfridge's, a prestigious department store. The demonstrations were a fiasco, Baird's apparatus working less well in the store than in the attic, to which it was returned for continuing development.

Illness kept Baird from working for several following weeks, and then he had a couple of good breaks. To his surprise, cousins in Scotland answered a plea for money with a check for five hundred pounds; and at about the same time, two London business firms offered to donate certain essential supplies.

The apparatus shown at Selfridge's had a rotating Nipkow disk that scanned the symbols to be transmitted and a photoelectric cell which modulated the current sent by wire to the receiver. A light beam in the receiver was modulated in intensity by incoming signals; the light swept over a ground-glass screen through a second Nipkow disk, which was supposed to rotate in perfect synchronization with the disk in the transmitter.

With the free supplies and the money from relatives, Baird was able to improve the quality of his equipment. On October 2, 1925, he was patiently transmitting his object—a ventriloquist's dummy nicknamed Bill. Previously the dummy's face had appeared on the receiver as a fuzzy outline with dark marks indicating the features of nose, eyes and mouth. But on that momentous October day, Bill's head took shape with features as well as hair and eyebrows fully defined.

The elated Baird rushed out of his workshop and literally dragged a teen-aged boy from an office in the same building. By coincidence Baird's first live model was another Bill, William Tayton, who years later was employed by Baird's television company. In return for half a crown, the reluctant model posed by the transmission device, and his face appeared on Baird's receiver set up in the next room.

Several members of the Royal Institution accepted Baird's invitation to see his television system on January 27, 1926. The occasion was a great success, and Baird even transmitted the face of a Royal Institution member, who minutes earlier had delayed the proceedings by getting his flowing white beard caught in the sending mechanism.

Very soon after, Baird gave his original invention to the South Kensington Science Museum and began to construct a more sophisticated and precise system. He continually strove to achieve better picture definition and, within a couple of

years, replaced the transmission wire with wireless telegraphy to increase the sending range.

In 1926, Baird invented his noctovisor, a device dependent on infrared light for making objects visible in the dark.
But he concentrated primarily on television, experimenting
with the sending of stereoscopic pictures and, at a meeting
in Glasgow in 1927, demonstrating one-inch-square color
television pictures, using a disk with three spirals of small
holes respectively covered with red, blue and green filters.

The mechanical perfection of Baird's invention did not
bring him immediate success, and the vexations and worries
of solitary and unsubsidized research were replaced by problems with business associates, both investors and promoters.

Applying for a license to transmit television, Baird encountered opposition from the British Broadcasting Corporation. Authorities stated flatly that any television system
in England would be initiated by the BBC, which was not
then in the least interested. Public pressure finally forced
a Parliamentary Committee to order the BBC to start television experiments. Baird on his own completed a satisfactory transatlantic transmission in 1928. Experimental
transmissions with Baird equipment were begun by the BBC
in September, 1929.

The first regular television programs of the BBC were produced at its London studios in Alexandra Palace in November, 1936. Baird was very much disappointed when the BBC
decided to transmit in alternate weeks by Baird's system,
still partially mechanical, and by the all-electronic American
system invented by V. K. Zworykin. The Baird mechanical

system scanned fewer lines than the electronic system which, as a result, produced sharper images on receiving sets.

During a German blitz in December, 1941, Baird telecast the first clear color-pictures of a dummy called Eustace; the papier-mâché doll, dressed in a pink hunting coat, blue pants, a sheik's headdress of bright yellow, had in its mouth a mechanical pipe that puffed out smoke.

Baird was ill in bed on the June day in 1946 when his last and finest television equipment received pictures transmitted by the BBC from a victory parade route in London. Within the week John Logie Baird was dead, at the age of fifty-eight.

Television, to which he gave his talent and energy, already established in England, was shortly to revolutionize the American way of life.

The breakthrough of a practical all-electronic system was made in the United States by Vladimir Kosma Zworykin. Born in Russia in 1889, he attended the Petrograd Institute of Technology and le Collège de France in Paris. After serving in the signal corps of the Russian Army during World War I, he migrated to the United States in 1919, and five years later became an American citizen.

At Petrograd (now Leningrad), Zworykin did two years of research with his professor, Boris Rosing. Rosing's experimentation with the Nipkow disk and the Braun tube indicated that the combination of a mechanical device and an electronic one was not practical. The project was dropped in 1912 because of the difficulties of attempting an all-electronic method at that time.

While Zworykin was with the Westinghouse Electric and Manufacturing Company in Pittsburgh, Pennsylvania, he received his Ph.D. from the University of Pittsburgh. From 1920 until 1929, he did research in Westinghouse laboratories, experimenting with photoelectric cells and, in 1923, inventing his iconoscope, an electronic camera tube. In the winter of 1923–1924, Zworykin demonstrated his "rudimentary all-electronic system for the transmission of pictures" to a group of Westinghouse executives.

About the demonstration he wrote, in 1952: "The system employed converted Westinghouse cathode-ray oscilloscope tubes for the pickup and receiving tube. The scanning rate was very low and the 'picture' merely an X-mark; clearly, the system shown was far removed from a practical television system. However, the pickup tube employed did incorporate the basic principle of the Iconoscope and the viewing tube of the Kinescope, however remote they may have appeared from present-day Iconoscopes and Kinescopes in details of physical construction and quality of performance."

In England, Baird concentrated on perfection of a mechanical television system; in the United States, development centered on nonmechanical scanning and reception, electronic systems to which Zworykin, Philo Taylor Farnsworth and others contributed. Farnsworth (1906–   ) was a teen-ager when he conceived the idea of televising pictures by the use of fast-flying electrons for scanning. At the age of twenty-one, he demonstrated a working model of his invention at the Crocker Research Laboratory in San Francisco and, at thirty-two, was the research director of the Farnsworth Television and Radio Corporation. His patented television inventions include a nonstorage camera tube, a dissector pickup tube, and numerous other devices essential to sending and receiving systems.

Unlike Baird, neither Farnsworth nor Zworykin worked in the isolation of a lonely attic; both had access to technological assistance. Zworykin became director of electronic research at the Radio Corporation of America Manufacturing Company in 1929, and associate research director of the RCA laboratories in 1942, serving afterward as director of electronic research.

Zworykin's iconoscope makes an electronic eye of the camera in which it is enclosed. By a lens, the image to be transmitted is cast on a plate within a vacuum tube. The plate, or mosaic, is covered with photosensitive spots insulated from each other. These become excited when light electrically charges them. The intensity of the charge depends on the amount of light falling on each microscopically sized spot. Again as with selenium, which was unsatisfactory because of its slow action, the more light the higher the charge, the less light the smaller the charge. The difference of light intensity gives the gradation necessary to form a picture.

From the mosaic the electrical charges speed along the tube of the iconoscope and are scanned by another beam of electrons. At the far end of the iconoscope, the picture is formed on an electronic gun, which sends the picture from the camera through complex electronic transmission devices to a viewing screen, the receiver, on which the picture is seen.

The Zworykin iconoscope was already successfully in operation by 1939 when two American inventors, Albert Rose and Harley Iam, introduced their invention, the image orthicon. It is a camera tube so sensitive that scenes can be transmitted even with the light of a candle. Needing less light than the iconoscope, the more sensitive image orthicon eventually replaced the earlier device.

Television, to which Zworykin made invaluable contributions, was on its way as a powerful medium of mass communication, the basis of a boundlessly influential and far-reaching industry.

AND AFTER

Postwar television development in the United States was marked by chronological crowding and commercial confusion: Inventions for improvement and expansion of telecasting followed one another in rapid succession. Receiving sets not uncommonly were outmoded between the date of purchase and the time of delivery to a home or business establishment. The Federal Communications Commission, unprepared for the inundation of applications from the television industry and for the mushroom growth of the television medium, made certain quick decisions that proved to be ill-advised.

The FCC arbitrarily ruled that all telecasting must be done over twelve channels of VHF, very-high-frequency bands. An advisable delay, allowing for due consideration, would wisely have resulted in selection of the seventy channels assigned to UHF, ultrahigh frequency.

In 1947, telecasting at irregular hours was provided by nineteen stations, their facilities having been converted from radiobroadcasting studios. The first television station to be housed in a building constructed for the purpose of telecasting was WAAM, in Baltimore, Maryland; its first program was transmitted in November, 1948. Planned, owned and operated by financier-brothers, Ben and Herman Cohen, WAAM was visited by interested American and foreign television people, both management representatives and technicians.

The range of commercial television, early limited to a community and its environs, was increased by the coaxial cable that carried both picture and sound. A coaxial cable is an encased tube of conducting metal, often copper; a conducting wire is centered in the tube. In 1935, a coaxial cable for telephone and telegraph was laid between New York and Philadelphia, and cables for message-sending steadily linked more cities. The first coast-to-coast telecast by coaxial cable was of the address given on September 4, 1951, by President Harry S Truman at the Japanese peace treaty conference in San Francisco. The use of coaxial cable for television permitted programs to be carried on a simultaneous network basis, first to dozens of American cities, then to hundreds of towns and thousands of rural communities.

Time-zone differences in the United States complicated commercial programming. A show produced "live" in New York at nine o'clock in the evening was simultaneously received in Los Angeles, but the time there was six o'clock, the dinner hour. The kinescope was the television industry's solution for showing entertainment programs in prime-time viewing hours on both coasts. The kine, a type of motion-picture film, had some drawbacks, chiefly a lack of clear and strong recorded images.

To replace the kine, a mechanical device, the industry introduced an electronic system for recording pictures and sound on magnetic tape. It makes possible the instant replay familiar to televiewers, particularly of sports and news programs.

Baird and many others after him experimented with color television. One method developed by the Columbia Broadcasting System was called field-sequential. In it a rotating disk, motor-driven and set behind the camera lens, has color segments of red, blue and green; light from the subject is filtered to pass through the system in succession. Black-and-white images received through the cathode-ray tube are converted to their original colors by a duplicate of the disk at the sending end.

The FCC, in 1950, again in a hasty acceptance, announced that the field-sequential system of CBS was to be the standard for color transmission. Color telecasts by that system did not, however, give satisfactory pictures on black-and-white sets. Other experimental color systems included the element-sequential developed by RCA. Light is broken up into the same three primary colors which are scanned in sequence by three pickups. After passing through complicated procedures, the pictures are received with good definition on both color and black-and-white sets; the system is what is called compatible, serving two purposes. In 1953 the FCC, reversing its 1950 decision, approved the RCA elemental sequential color system as standard.

In part because of the poor quality of the first color telecasts and primarily because of the high cost of color sets, color television was slow in catching on. It was to be more than a decade after the second FCC ruling before color was popularly accepted by televiewers and available to a mass public.

Cameras were redesigned for the improvement of commercial telecasting, and new types were invented for non-commercial uses outside the confines of broadcast studios.

One of the first very small cameras designed for research was developed by Dr. Arthur Parpart, a Princeton University biologist, who worked in close cooperation with Zworykin at the RCA laboratories in Princeton, New Jersey. Parpart's small vidicon camera can be placed over the eyepiece of a microscope for observation of specimen-material on the microscope stage. Active images of the microscopic material, grossly enlarged by the vidicon camera, are viewed on a connected television screen. That device, providing a new technique for scientific research, was first publicly demonstrated in the spring of 1951 on *The Johns Hopkins Science Review,* a weekly network television program.

The potential of television to education is far from realized today. Television is presently a teaching aid in classrooms at primary and secondary schools, at colleges and universities; and its future is assured for programs of instruction and for presentation of lectures by eminent scholars in distant places. How widely and wisely the medium will be used depends on the creativity and imagination of educators capable of understanding the scope of television and of utilizing its techniques.

Today's television cameras with their sensitivity to small amounts of light are operable almost anyplace; there is no way to escape their probing eye. Small models, portable and sized for installation in a little space, are being used in manufacturing plants, laboratories, courtrooms; at meetings and official hearings; and as security devices in banks and stores.

UHF transmission, because of the earth's curvature, requires cable connections or relay stations: towers, airborne craft or satellites. The first transatlantic telecast via the communication satellite Telstar was transmitted on July 10, 1962. The television camera orbiting in space is an instrument for research, military observation, and relay of entertainment programs.

Television's range, limited during early experimentation to a few feet, is already global. In the foreseeable future, it will be interplanetary.

INDEX